GREENLY'S
MODEL STEAM LOCOMOTIVE
DESIGNS AND SPECIFICATIONS

REVISED BY

ERNEST A. STEEL

Assoc.I.Mech.E., M.J.I.E.

With 36 Illustrations including
20 Practical Working Designs

© The Estates of Henry Greenly & Ernest A. Steel 2011

First edition   1952
Published by Cassell & Company Limited

This edition   2011

British Library Cataloguing-in-Publication-Data:
a catalogue record of this book is held by the British Library.

ISBN No. 0-9564073-8-2

Published in Great Britain by:
CAMDEN MINIATURE STEAM SERVICES
Barrow Farm, Rode, Frome, Somerset. BA11 6PS U.K.
www.camdenmin.co.uk

Camden stock one of the widest selections of model engineering, technical and
transportation books to be found.
Contact them at the above address for a copy of their latest free Booklist.

Printed by Salisbury Printing Company Limited.

PLEASE NOTE!
In this book the authors and publisher are only passing on knowledge, some of which
may have been overtaken by the march of time and technology, such as the use of
asbestos wicks in the burners of spirit fired models.
Your safety, and that of others, is your responsibility, both in the workshop and when
running any locomotive in your care.

CONTENTS

LIST OF DESIGNS

INTRODUCTION

THE first book by Henry Greenly dealing with the construction and design of model steam locomotives appeared as long ago as 1904 and at a time when model making was not as widespread as it is to-day (*The Model Locomotive*, P. Marshall & Co.). In 1922 there appeared the first edition of his main work, *Model Steam Locomotives*, which, running into several editions until 1939, has remained a standard text-book for model engineers throughout the English-speaking world. A further handbook from his pen (and drawing-board) was published in 1934. In it Mr. Greenly gathered together a comprehensive collection of locomotive designs ranging from a simple model in No. o gauge to the more powerful 5-inch gauge type eminently suitable for passenger-hauling purposes in a garden or for demonstrations at garden fêtes. In this way he was able to give instructions and to lay down specifications for various designs which supplemented to a considerable extent the principles embodied in the main work, *Model Steam Locomotives*.

In view of the phenomenal increase since the war in the number of amateur model makers, model engineers, and societies and clubs devoted to the building of model steam locomotives, it has been considered desirable to revise the old edition of this book completely. Models of well-known British and American prototypes of twenty-five years ago are retained in this edition, together with those of modern types now in service. The simple type of 2–4–2 tank engine in No. o gauge with its single inside slide-valve cylinder is retained for the beginner to make a start upon. Once having mastered the construction of the engine and run it successfully on a length of track, he will be keen to advance a step farther and build another model engine of more ambitious dimensions. It is with this object in view that a number of the designs have been specially selected—not forgetting those more experienced model makers who specialize in gauges ranging from No. 1 to 7¼-inch and who are seeking further designs for construction in the workshop and to run on their own or club tracks.

Many of the well-known model engineering firms stock standard parts to suit the standard gauges up to and including 7¼-inch. These comprise such parts as buffers, draw-hooks, wheels, axles, cylinders, and boiler fittings—to mention but a few. For the larger gauges a fairly comprehensive range of castings is usually obtainable so that parts can be machined and finished in the home workshop, or the parts may even be supplied machined and ready for assembly.

Although probably beyond the range—and the means of the average model maker—a chapter is devoted to large-scale locomotives ranging from 9½- to 15-inch gauge. No apology is offered for specifying an engine over one-quarter full-size and weighing with its tender over five tons, as the author is of the opinion that, for those engineers who plan to put down a large passenger-carrying miniature railway, whether at home or overseas, these notes will enable them to choose a design to suit their requirements. There are many of these miniature locomotives in service to-day—many of them having been built by well-known British engineering firms who have had many years of experience in this class of work.

Readers who desire the fullest information on the subject of model locomotive design and construction are recommended to refer to the new and completely revised edition of *Model Steam Locomotives* by Henry Greenly, price 15/-, published by Cassell and Co. Ltd.

E. A. STEEL

GREENLY'S MODEL LOCOMOTIVE DESIGNS AND SPECIFICATIONS

CHAPTER I

FUNDAMENTALS OF DESIGN

In any working model locomotive that is provided with a boiler and a system of firing that will ensure a continuous head of steam, the hauling power of the model will depend on the weight on the driving wheels, the size of the cylinders, and steam pressure.

The weight on the coupled wheels must be sufficient to prevent the wheels from slipping.

If the cylinders are made too large, of course, they will tend to drain the boiler of steam, and even if the fire is intense enough to maintain sufficient steam, the available water will be exhausted all the sooner. To a certain limited extent a cylinder larger than the normal may be employed with success if, as explained later, the steam pressure can be kept back in the boiler

The designs given in this book show the proportions of cylinders usually adopted for models of various scales, and larger sizes than those specified should only be adopted where the boilers are of maximum proportions and high efficiency.

It is usual to fire models of 2½-inch gauge and upwards with charcoal or coal. For smaller gauges methylated spirit, burnt in a simple lamp, is quite the most satisfactory fuel, although paraffin or petrol used in a burner of the blow-lamp type can be employed. The methylated spirit vaporizing lamp is really only suitable for models which have outside fired natural draught boilers.

All very small locomotives need to be built with boilers of relatively thin plates (subject to a hydraulic test) so that the heat of the burners is more easily transferred to the water inside. For No. o and No. 1 gauge models this is an essential to success, and therefore high pressures which would require the use of thick plates should not be adopted.

Firing Small Locomotives

Where methylated spirit flame is entirely enclosed in a furnace, i.e. a firebox, then an induced draught similar to that provided in a real locomotive, and also in a coal-fired working model, must be provided. A fierce draught is not required, as a spirit lamp burns best under more gentle conditions than charcoal or coal. At the same time a leaky smoke-box must be avoided. Complete air tightness in the construction and fitting of the door and smokebox chamber is very necessary so that the exhaust steam from the blast pipe shall properly induce air through the fire.

While the size of the exhaust nozzle is important, the disposition of the blast pipe in relation to the chimney must be reasonably correct to obtain the best results. There is no magic about the matter, and if the rule given below is not adhered to more or less accurately, an abject failure to 'steam' is likely to result. The effect is, however, truly magical where an engine wrongly proportioned in this respect is altered from an incorrect to the correct arrangement.

TABLE I

BLAST PIPE ORIFICES

(For two-cylinder schemes)

Cylinder bore Inches	Diameter of orifice Inches	Notes
$\frac{3}{8}$	$\frac{1}{16}$	Free exhaust[1]
$\frac{1}{2}$	$\frac{3}{32}-\frac{7}{64}$	Sharp to mild blast
$\frac{5}{8}$	$\frac{7}{64}-\frac{1}{8}$	Sharp to mild blast
$\frac{3}{4}$	$\frac{1}{8}-\frac{5}{32}$	Sharp to mild blast
1	$\frac{11}{64}$	
$1\frac{1}{4}$	$\frac{7}{32}$	
$1\frac{1}{2}$	$\frac{1}{4}$	See note below[2]
$1\frac{3}{4}$	$\frac{9}{32}$	
2	$\frac{11}{32}$	

[1] Where spirit firing is employed a milder draught is required, as with a fierce blast the flames will be drawn from the wicks.

[2] For three- and four-cylinder engines, orifices are 20% and 40% larger in diameter respectively.

The invention of the blast pipe was one of the chief items which led to the success of the railway locomotive in its early days and it is still a feature which receives considerable attention from the locomotive engineer.

For model-making purposes after the size of the blast nozzle has been determined (Table I) its position may be settled by making two templates of brass and inserting them down the chimney (Figs. 1 and 2). The chosen angles remain the same whatever the size of the locomotive. The only other points are to see that the correct size and position has been obtained, that the blast nozzle is concentric with the chimney, and that the jet of exhaust steam delivered is truly in line with the centre of the chimney.

The chief reason why it is difficult to make a scale model in No. o gauge to work by steam is that it is not possible to scale down the space required above the flame of the lamp; and also the rate of consumption of water is larger in proportion to its size than that obtained in a model of larger scale and gauge. Of course if the maker does not mind the boiler being pitched very high, then a certain amount of success can be expected. It is essential that a space not less than $\frac{3}{4}$-inch high should intervene between the top of the wicks and the bottom of the boiler; $\frac{7}{8}$ or 1 inch would improve matters.

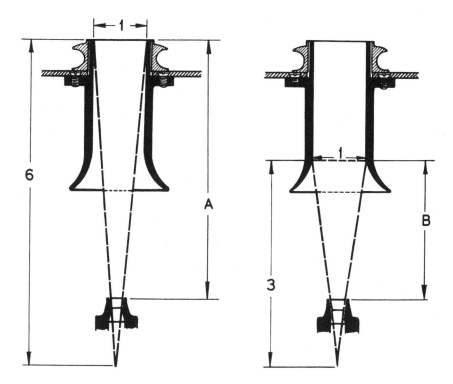

Fig. 1. To find the height of the blast pipe, cut a 1 in 6 sheet-metal template.
The height A is then determined, the template fitting in the top of the funnel

Fig. 2. To set the internal extension of the funnel, cut a template to fit inside the
funnel with a 1 in 3 taper to it. The extension of the funnel inside the smokebox
should coincide with the parallel portion of the template, or, in other words, the
dimension B is determined

Superheating the Steam

Steam generated in a boiler is said to be 'saturated' and, at a given
pressure, has a given temperature as a reference to standard steam tables
will show. Thus, steam at atmospheric pressure (14·7 lb. per square inch)
has a temperature corresponding to that of boiling water (212°F.). At
50 lb. per square inch it is raised to 298°F., and at 100 lb. the temperature
is 338°F., and so on. Wet steam must be avoided, as it leads to losses by
condensation in pipes and cylinders. Therefore, in order to ensure some
degree of dryness, additional heat should be given to the steam so that its
temperature is increased above that obtaining for the particular pressure.
This increased temperature or 'degrees of superheat' is a useful property,
particularly for large models where maximum efficiency is desirable.
Conversely, superheating can be effected by 'wire-drawing' or expanding

the steam to a lower pressure without loss of heat from it to any appreciable extent.

Superheating is accomplished by leading the steam through the flues where a higher temperature than that of the boiler itself (and the steam) obtains. In a small working model, owing to the thinness of the plates, a reasonable efficiency is obtained and both smokebox and fire-tube superheaters can only be moderately successful. Drying the steam is more easily effected by 'wire-drawing'. It can be done by employing small ports, but is more successful if it is done at the main stop valve (the regulator), as the steam can then expand in a warm place, i.e. in the boiler or the smoke-box. This fact explains why an engine with over-size cylinders is very often almost as successful as one with cylinders of the normal dimension.

Expanding it to a lower pressure in pipes which are arranged in a situation which is as hot or hotter than the steam at the higher pressure provides dry steam at a higher temperature than the normal one. This superheating by wire-drawing is best done by passing it through a little hole of short length, not through a long small-diameter tube.

Tractive Effort

Cylinder and boiler dimensions depend on the particular design of locomotive concerned and proportions must be arranged to suit each other. The bore of the cylinders should not be made too large; and special attention should be given to correct firing, proper alignment of blast pipe and chimney, and balanced steam distribution in the cylinders.

To avoid slipping on the rail, the total weight on the driving and coupled wheels should not be much less than four times the nominal tractive power exerted by the cylinders on the treads of the wheels.

Thus, tractive force $(\text{T.F.}) = \dfrac{D^2 \times S \times P}{W}$.

Where D = Diameter of cylinder, S = Stroke
$\quad\quad\quad P$ = Boiler pressure in lb. per square inch, and
$\quad\quad\quad W$ = Diameter of driving wheels.
$\quad\quad\quad\quad$ (D, S, and W are measured in inches.)

For small models the tractive force is approximately 60% of the values calculated by the above formula and for large models (over 1-inch scale) it is about 80%. In real practice a figure of 85% of the boiler pressure is usually employed.

For a No. o gauge model various component parts and accessories are available for the convenience of the beginner and are to be found in the trade catalogues. Most of the well-known firms stock wheels, axles, safety valves, chimneys, cylinders, and buffers, etc. The same applies equally well for No. 1 gauge. For the remainder of materials for construction, a certain measure of skill in the working of sheet metal, fitting, and turning is required.

In the construction of No. o and No. 1 gauge models the metric system of measurement is generally employed. The scale for No. o gauge is 7 mm.

to the foot, and for No. 1 gauge it is 10 mm. to the foot. The British system is used, however, for drills, taps, and dies, and stock materials.

As the model becomes larger in scale it is necessary to add to the details, not only because the increase in mere size allows the amateur engineer to make certain component parts otherwise impossible or difficult, but by reason of the fact that the magnitude of the destructive forces are greater in proportion. For example, in a diminutive model the axles may be made to run in simple bushes in the frames. Where the springing of the axles are essential to successful running, as in locomotive models larger than No. 0 (32 mm.) gauge machines, axle-boxes are made separately and are grooved to slide in slots in the frames. Such sprung axle-boxes will, however, not stand wear and tear for lengthy periods in models of 2½-inch gauge and larger, and it is, in such engines, common practice to reinforce the frame slots with cast gunmetal, cast iron, or steel horn-plates. These increase the bearing area of the boxes.

TABLE II

STANDARD DIMENSIONS

	Gauge					
	No. 0	No. 1	2½-in.	3½-in.	5-in.	7¼-in.
Scale: mm. to the foot	7	10	14	19	28	38
Fraction of full size	1/43	1/31	1/22	1/16	1/11	1/8
Scale: inches to the foot	9/32	0·4	9/16	¾	1·1	1½
Rail gauge	32 mm.	45 mm.	2½	3½	5	7¼
Scale tons (1 lb.) =	12½ tons	5½ tons	2¼ tons	1 ton	6½ cwt.	3 cwt.
Maximum width (inches)	2½	3⅝	5	6¾	10¼	13½
Maximum height (inches)	3¾	5	7½	10	15	20
Maximum speed: feet per min.	110	300	440	550	700	880
Type of fuel	Spirit	Spirit or Coal	Spirit or Coal	Coal	Coal	Coal

Engines with small driving wheels are as a general rule more successful models than those with large wheels, simply because the piston speed (i.e. the revolutions per minute) is higher and condensation losses are reduced. Where the firebox comes over a coupled axle, a deeper box, and more capacious furnace, is also possible with wheels of a smaller diameter.

For all two-cylinder schemes, whether inside or outside the frames, cranks are set at 90° to each other. The right-hand crank usually leads in the forward direction when viewed from the cab. There are exceptional cases of left-hand cranks leading.

CHAPTER II

CYLINDERS AND VALVE GEAR

As the general outline of a working model steam locomotive depends so largely on the particular disposition of the cylinder and its connecting mechanism, this chapter comprises a series of cylinder and motion arrangements to guide the reader in his choice of a prototype, and these are included or are referred to later on in individual designs specified within these covers.

In a steam locomotive the chassis should provide, firstly, for a set of driving wheels arranged with a wheelbase suited to the driving mechanism and which, at the same time, will negotiate the curves of the railway. Secondly, the wheels and motion should allow room for the firebox and, where used, the lamp which takes the place of a furnace burning solid fuel. Finally, the carrying of the supply of water and fuel will, of course, determine whether the model is to be a tank locomotive or a tender engine.

No. 0 Gauge. Single Inside Cylinder Arrangement

The design (Fig. 3) is a detail drawing of a cylinder and valve motion which can be made by any beginner for a No. o gauge locomotive. The single double-acting slide valve cylinder is located between the frames with the steam chest at the side, and a direct acting slip eccentric reversing valve gear. This scheme may be applied to any model inside cylinder locomotive. If instead of a leading bogie there is a coupled driving wheel in front of the crank axle, then the mechanism will have to be inclined to clear the leading axle. Such inclination may also be required to lift the cylinder above a bogie mechanism where the driving wheels are of small diameter.

The single inside cylinder scheme may be enlarged to suit a 1¾-inch gauge locomotive. The slip eccentric reversing gear is sufficiently good for single-cylinder engines having a dead point in starting. Reversing is automatic, simply by pushing the engine a short distance in the direction required for the engine to travel. There is no operating gear in the cab.

Specification

Cylinder. ¾-inch bore by ⅝-inch stroke. Brass or gun-metal.
Valve. Double-acting slide valve. Steam ports $\frac{1}{16}$-inch holes. Exhaust ports $\frac{3}{32}$-inch holes. Lap of valve $\frac{1}{32}$ inch. Travel of valve $\frac{3}{16}$ inch.
Valve Gear. Slip eccentric with stop collar.
Crosshead Slide. Overhead flat bar.
Connecting Rod. Normal type fitted to crosshead. The big end can be modified and the standard split bush and cover with two bolts fitted.

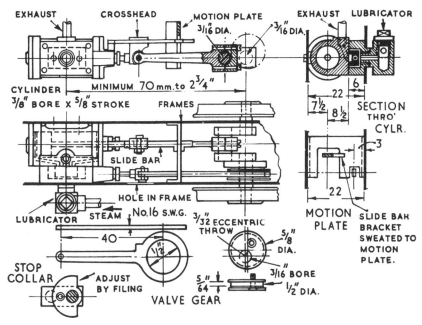

Fig. 3. Arrangement of Single Inside Cylinder

Crank Axle. Built up with $\frac{3}{16}$-inch round mild steel, webs $\frac{1}{8}$- by $\frac{5}{16}$-inch rectangular steel bar, drilled in pairs, and pinned and soft soldered or brazed to axle. Alternatively the axle may be turned from a solid bar.

No. 1 Gauge. Outside Cylinders with Inside Slip Eccentric

While the single-cylinder scheme, as in the preceding design, may be adopted for No. 1 gauge locomotives, the more ambitious model maker will prefer a two-cylinder (double-acting) mechanism and for this form of drive the simplest reversing gear is the direct acting slip eccentric motion placed inside the frames, as illustrated in the detail drawing (Fig. 4).

This mechanism will suit any outside cylinder locomotive, but as shown it is particularly useful for four- or six-coupled engines in which the outside cylinder is set midway between the bogie wheels. As exemplified, it is a part of a design for a 4-4-0 engine. For a 4-6-0 locomotive the drive would be taken by the second coupled axle, and longer connecting and eccentric rods would have to be used.

The cylinders are set horizontally—as shown—or only slightly inclined to the driving axle for engines with large (2½-inch diameter) coupled wheels. Where small drivers are employed the cylinders should be inclined from a centre line approximately 1¼ inches above the rail level.

Specification

Cylinders. Standard extended steam chest type $\frac{1}{2}$-inch bore by $\frac{3}{4}$-inch stroke. Placed outside the frames and supported on a pad piece thickening up the main frames locally.

Valves. Ordinary slide valves with $\frac{1}{20}$-inch lap and $\frac{7}{32}$ inch total travel.

Valve Gear. Slip eccentric reversing gear, loose sheave driven by a duplex stop collar through a pin driven in the inside of the sheave. Driving faces of stop collar must be exactly at right angles. Adjust port opening by filing driving faces of stop collar.

Slide Bars. Double round bar $\frac{3}{32}$-inch diameter.

Crosshead. Modified 'Laird' or single-bar type, drilled for slide bars.

Exhaust Pipe. $\frac{3}{16}$-inch diameter Breeches type. Exhaust nozzle $\frac{5}{64}$-inch diameter, approximately.

Steam Pipe. $\frac{5}{32}$-inch diameter with cross connection piece joining the two steam chests in the centre.

No. 1 Gauge. Outside Cylinders with Outside Valve Gear

The cylinders and the whole of the motion parts are outside the wheels and frames. The valves are on top of the cylinders slightly offset to the outside, as shown in the end view (Fig. 5). The driving wheels are mounted on the second coupled axle from the leading end, and the exterior outline of the cylinder body is modelled to represent the latest pattern of piston-valve cylinders.

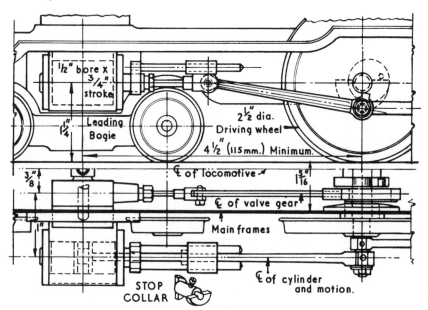

Fig. 4. Outside Cylinders with Inside Valve Gear

The cylinder and wheel arrangement will suit models of the 'Atlantic' 4–4–2 type, 4–6–0 and 'Pacific' 4–6–2 type locomotives. Where smaller driving wheels are used the cylinders and motion would be inclined and the scheme applied to 4–8–0 and 4–8–2 mountain type engines with equal ease.

The valve motion is the Greenly's fully corrected modification of Joy's valve gear, in which the links driven off the end of the connecting rod crank-pin, move a die in the 'Joy' type slide or weigh shaft.

This shaft is illustrated in Fig. 5. To effect the reversal of the loco-motive the weigh shaft is tilted either forward or backward of the central, neutral, or mid-gear position. If the engine is fitted on sprung axle-boxes it is desirable to place the actual driving axle on rather stiff springs to limit the vertical movement.

The gear is suitable for any size of engine up to and including those for 7¼-inch gauge garden railways. It is simpler to make than Walschaerts' valve gear, the standard gear of the kind used on large engines, but in appearance it is much the same.

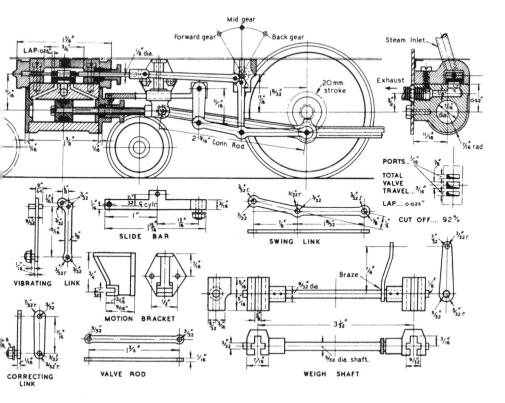

Fig. 5. Outside Cylinders with Outside Valve Gear

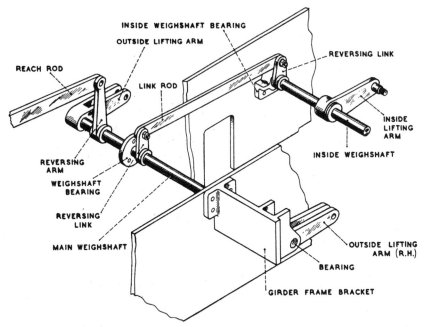

Fig. 6. Weigh Shafts for a Three-cylinder Locomotive. (See p. 52)

Specification

Cylinders. $\frac{7}{16}$-inch bore by 20-mm. stroke. Valves on top.

Valves. Slide valve type above the pistons, actuated by direct Greenly's type valve gear.

Slide Bars. Single-bar type provided with a lug, fixed to a slide bar bracket from the frames. The slide bar carries the pivot for the anchor connecting link of the valve gear.

Crosshead. Laird single-bar type, with jaw or open at the back to embrace the slide bar.

Swing Link. The swing link of valve gear attached at one end to the lower pivot of anchor link, the other end fitting the crank-pin outside the connecting rod.

Vibrating Link. Made in pairs, and pivoted to the swing link near the centre. The top end is formed with a forward projection. The lower hole is fitted with a pin extended to fit the tilting reversing slide, the upper one with a $\frac{1}{16}$-inch pin for the valve rod.

Valve Setting. Bend the swing link or raise or lower the driving axle so that on dead centre the valve rod does not move when the reverse lever is moved from fore gear to back gear. Then adjust the valve for equal travel over the ports.

Ports. Steam ports; one $\frac{3}{32}$ inch to each end of the cylinder. Exhaust, two $\frac{5}{64}$-inch holes meeting $\frac{7}{64}$-inch 'exhaust passage', lap of valve $\frac{1}{32}$ inch. Maximum travel of valve $\frac{7}{32}$ inch.

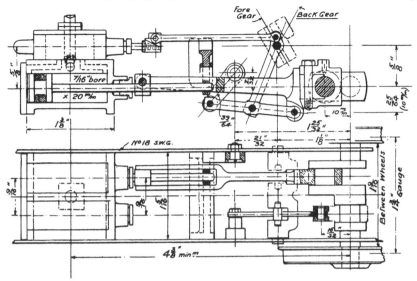

Fig. 7. Arrangement of No. 1 Gauge Inside Cylinders and Motion

Reversing Shaft. Maximum angle of tilt 30° from the vertical in each direction.

No. 1. Gauge Inside Cylinders and Motion with Reversing Valve Gear

This mechanism (Fig. 7) can be arranged to suit any engine of the inside cylinder design, and is more particularly applicable to 4–4–0 express engines and 0–6–0 type heavy goods locomotives.

The valve gear is of the Greenly type which, like Joy's valve gear used in full-size practice, eliminates the four eccentrics between the cranks necessary in the well-known Stephenson's valve gear. This last-named gear is almost impossible in a No. 1 gauge working model and not too easy in 2½-inch gauge. The advantage of the present gear in a small gauge of model over the ordinary Joy's is that the pins being clear of the connecting rod, may be of more robust size.

The two cylinders are cast in one block and the valves are placed on top. This arrangement, shown in Fig. 8, is a standard one devised by the writer many years ago. The steam chest is common to both slide valves, and the exhaust passages are drilled in the block and are brought out by a pipe passing through the live steam chest.

The system of operating the reversing gear is the same as for the outside valve gear illustrated in the previous design, but everything is contained within the inside framing of the engine. As the swing link cannot be attached direct to the crank-pin it is pivoted on a lug on the connecting rod. The anchor correcting link is pivoted to the main frames, as shown in Fig. 7.

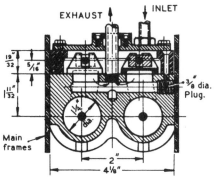

Fig. 8. Cross Section of Inside Cylinders

The gear, with modifications, can be used on any size of model larger than No. 1 gauge and is useful as the inside valve gear of a four-cylinder model.

For small-wheeled engines the whole gear must be inclined downwards to the driving axle.

Specification

Cylinder. Twin double-acting slide valve cylinder cast in one block with separate steam chest and top cover. Bore $\frac{7}{16}$ inch, stroke 20 mm., fitting between frames $1\frac{5}{16}$ inches apart (Fig. 8).

Valves. Slide valves placed directly above the cylinders in a steam chest common to both valves. Steam ports $\frac{1}{16}$ by $\frac{1}{8}$ inch; exhaust ports $\frac{3}{32}$ by $\frac{1}{8}$ inch, lap $\frac{1}{32}$ inch; maximum travel of valves $\frac{7}{32}$ inch.

Crank Axle. Built from $\frac{5}{16}$-inch diameter steel bar with webs $\frac{1}{8}$-inch and $\frac{5}{32}$-inch thick by $\frac{7}{16}$-inch wide, flat bar, pinned on and soft soldered or brazed. Axle may be turned from solid bar.

Connecting Rod. Cast gun-metal with strap for big end and forked little end. Offset little end to accommodate a straight-through gudgeon-pin.

Piston Rod Guide. Direct forked connecting-rod type supporting extension of piston rod. Cast gun-metal machined to fit between frames.

Reversing Slide Shaft. Made from a gun-metal casting with both slides machined out of the solid. Angle of tilt in full gear not more than 30° each side of the central (mid-gear) position.

Stephenson's Link Motion for Outside Cylinder Engines

The reversing gear introduced by George Stephenson and known under his name is still very largely used by locomotive engineers. As exemplified by the accompanying design (Fig. 9), it is very applicable to outside cylinder engines, the motion being inside the framing. Where the valve gear is used for an 'Atlantic' or 4-6-0 type engine, as shown, the eccentric rods may have to be bent to clear the leading coupled axle.

With parts made more robust in proportion, the design may be applied to $1\frac{3}{4}$-inch gauge and be used instead of a slip eccentric reversing gear. As dimensioned in the drawing, the gear is arranged for a $2\frac{1}{2}$-inch gauge locomotive, but the gear is very adaptable to any larger-gauge model having the particular wheel and firebox arrangements indicated.

Specification

Cylinders. Outside the frames, driving on to the second coupled axle.

Valve Chests. Vertical valve faces inside the frames.

Valve Motion. Stephenson's reversing gear; direct acting working on to an intermediate valve spindle guided in a cross stretcher fitted between the main frames.

Eccentrics. Inside the frames, two for each valve.

Reversing or Weigh Shaft. Placed above the valve motion with lifting links pinned to the bottom of the Stephenson curved expansion link.

Walschaerts' Valve Gear, 1-inch Scale, 5-inch Gauge Design

Walschaerts' valve gear combined with outside cylinders having piston-type valves on the top of the cylinders is a gear that is used on modern locomotives throughout the world. As a valve motion it can hardly be surpassed and all larger models should be fitted with it, if the cylinder arrangements make it applicable.

The drawing (Fig. 10) exemplifies this motion on a model 1-inch scale, 5-inch gauge, 4–6–0 type express locomotive of the Southern Region 'King Arthur' class. The drawing can be used with the dimensions reduced to half-size for a 2½-inch gauge model with the same wheel arrangements.

As drawn, the valve gear is designed for piston-valve cylinders, but if slide valve cylinders are used, the gear must be arranged with the return crank on the opposite quarter and the lap and lead pins of the crosshead link reversed. This entails a new setting-out of the gear.

Walschaerts' valve gear is a difficult gear to standardize and practically every type of locomotive requires a different setting-out of the parts. Therefore the full-size blueprints issued by the author for various models should be consulted in every case.

Specification

Cylinders. Cast iron. Outside type with valves above the pistons $1\frac{7}{16}$-inch bore by $2\frac{1}{4}$-inch stroke.

Valves. $\frac{7}{8}$-inch diameter piston valves, inside admission and double ported. Fitted in cast-iron liners (Fig. 11).

Piston Rings. Metal spring rings, cast iron.

Expansion Links. Box-type links, mild steel, case hardened, pivoted on double valve gear frames, driven by straight eccentric rods to the outer member of the box link.

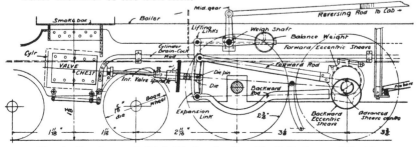

Fig. 9. Stephenson's Link Motion for Outside Cylinders and Inside Valve Chests

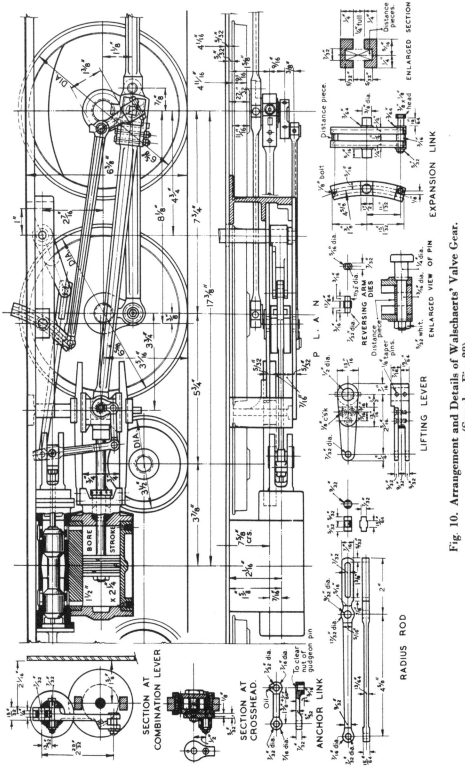

Fig. 10. Arrangement and Details of Walschaerts' Valve Gear.
(See also Fig. 28)

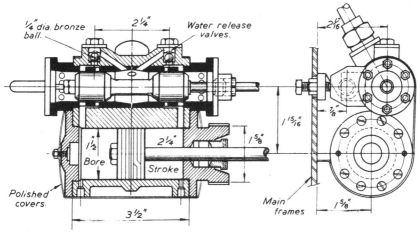

Fig. 11. 1-inch Scale Double-ported Piston-valve Cylinder

Lifting Links. Slide-type lifting arm with built-up lever. All joints not bushed to be case hardened.

Return Crank. Trailing type for inside admission with square end, split for bolting to crank-pin.

Wheels. Cast iron throughout.

Connecting Rod. Mild steel fluted, with strap for big end. Bushed at little end with bronze.

Coupling Rods. Fluted and jointed rods. Ends bushed with bronze.

Crossheads. Two-bar type, made in three pieces with gun-metal slippers.

Valve Spindles. Guided by four gun-metal bushes machined out of solid. All steel motion parts case hardened and machine work finished bright. Stainless steel also used.

STEAM PORT PROPORTIONS (SLIDE VALVES)

As a guide to steam port proportions for slide valves the following particulars are given:

Length of ports	$\frac{1}{2}$ diameter of cylinder
Width of steam ports	$\frac{1}{16}$ length of stroke
Width of exhaust ports	$\frac{1}{8}$ length of stroke
Width of port bars	$\frac{5}{64}$ length of stroke

For larger models add $\frac{1}{16}$ inch to the result obtained for the length of the ports.

Note.—Ports of excessive length are bad, as the loads on the valve and valve gear are increased enormously, and wear is rapid.

No actual lead is necessary in small models, but lap is essential. The average amount of lap is one-half of the width of the steam ports, giving about 86% cut-off.

CHAPTER III

DESIGN OF BOILERS

THERE are two main types of boilers employed on model locomotives to-day: (1) the water-tube type with its methylated spirit wick burners, and (2) the orthodox solid-fuel loco-type boiler that functions in exactly the same way as its full-size prototype on main-line railways. Liquid fuel is sometimes used for model boilers as in real practice. Of the two types, the solid-fuel boiler is undoubtedly the most popular. Nevertheless, for the all-important purpose of steam raising, the spirit-fired boiler still has a place in the smaller-scale model railway, a position it has held for well over a half-century.

WATER-TUBE BOILERS

For all amateur-made models using the methylated spirit wick lamp the boiler invented by F. Smithies in 1900 is the best type. The external shell is formed to agree with outline of the finished boiler and designed in accordance with the prototype. The inner boiler, the boiler proper, is suspended inside at the top of the outer casing and, to promote the best circulation of water, has several water-tubes silver soldered to it, as indicated in the design for a No. 1 gauge boiler, and shown in part section in Fig. 12.

This boiler requires a wick lamp. The vaporizing lamp used for boilers which work under natural draught is not suitable, because in these water-tube boilers there is an enclosed flue and this requires a draught induced in the chimney by the action of the exhaust steam in the blast pipe from the cylinders to draw the products of combustion through it.

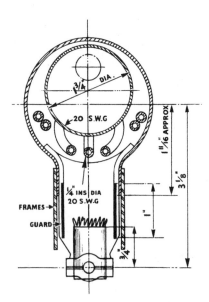

Fig. 12. Section through Water-tube Boiler

Specification for No. 1 Gauge Water-tube Boiler

Type. Boiler for 4–4–0 type locomotive with round-topped firebox

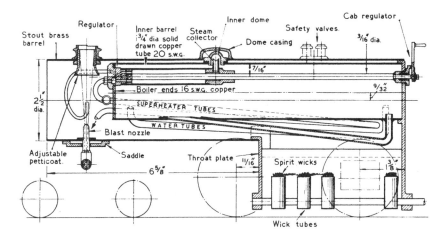

Fig. 13. Spirit-fired Boiler of the 'Smithies' type

narrowed in between the wheels and frames. Boiler can be modified and extended in length to suit a 4–6–0 type locomotive if required.

Outer Shell. Stout 2½-inch barrel, brass or sheet steel, with circular smoke-box supported on a cast gun-metal saddle at front end.

Inner Barrel. 1¾-inch gauge copper tube walls 24 s.w.g. thick. With stout No. 18 or No. 16 s.w.g. ends. The back end may be integral with the back plate, as shown in Fig. 13, or a separate circular flanged plate and projecting through a hole in the back plate, as shown in locomotive design No. 2. All joints subject to steam pressure silver soldered

Regulator. Steam taken from a hollow filler plug under dome casing to a semi-rotary valve near smokebox comprising both blower and main steam supply to superheater and cylinders.

Superheater. Bent-back type, where two separate cylinders are used the steam pipe should be divided into two at the smokebox, and a twin pipe, one each side of the inner boiler, bent back to the furnace.

Water-tubes. Three longitudinal water-tubes $\frac{7}{32}$ inch, all joints to barrel silver soldered.

Wick Burner. Tubes, four oval or rectangular tubes, disposed to clear coupled axles.

Working Pressure. 40 to 45 lb. per square inch.

Safety Valves. Special model 'Ross' type pop valves or one standard direct loaded valve.

Constructional Note. As the inner boiler is suspended in the flame all joints to ends and water-tubes, also pad pieces for screwed-in fittings should be silver soldered, not brazed. Soft soldering has been used for fixing ends, but is likely to lead to trouble if the process is applied to the fixing of water-tubes.

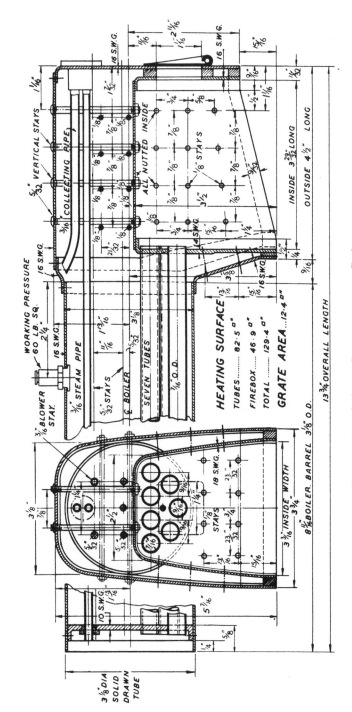

Fig. 14. 2½-inch Gauge Locomotive-type Boiler

LOCOMOTIVE-TYPE FIRE-TUBE BOILERS

Boilers for Small Scale Locomotives

The orthodox locomotive-type boiler consists of a horizontal barrel fitted to a water-enclosed firebox at the rear end. The firebox is usually oblong, but where it is not restricted by frames or wheels it can be made wider, or as wide as the diameter of the barrel. The furnace has the usual fire grate and communicates with the smokebox at the front end of the barrel by means of a more or less large number of small diameter flue-tubes. The inside firebox walls and the flue-tubes provide the heating surface.

The flat sides of the firebox require staying against the bursting tendency of the 'water legs' between them. The fire is fed through a steam-tight hole in the back plate of the boiler.

Specification for $\frac{1}{2}$-inch Scale Boiler

Construction (Fig. 14). While castings can be employed they are best fitted where mechanical methods of securing joints are used, soft solder being the caulking material. Where silver soldering is employed a lesser amount of riveting or screwing up is necessary, but the plate should be of copper flanged over where necessary by pressing or hammering. Riveting and screwing may be used in conjunction with flanged copper plates and soft-soldered seams, but the soldering must not be considered as adding anything to the strength of the boiler in resisting the bursting pressure.

Tubes may be screwed in at the firebox end by using 40 threads per inch.

Boiler Barrel. $3\frac{1}{8}$-inch solid drawn copper tube, No. 18 s.w.g. thick.

Firebox. Outside No. 16 s.w.g. plates. Inner, No. 18 gauge wrapper plates, No. 16 gauge tube and back plates.

Tubes. $\frac{7}{16}$-inch outside diameter, No. 20 gauge thick.

Staying. Direct screwed copper stays. $\frac{1}{8}$- or $\frac{5}{32}$-inch diameter, 40 threads or equivalent BA sizes.

Regulator. Plug type on back plate with collecting pipe, or semi-rotary valve at smokebox end operated by reach-rod through boiler and handle on back plate.

Large Boilers

Large boilers are almost invariably made to burn solid fuel, and a careful choice of prototype is desirable so that the greatest capacity and largest grate area can be obtained. Capacity of firebox is more important than grate area in any engine where the driver does not sit behind it. The maximum length of run is determined by the volume of the fuel carried in the furnace. The wheel arrangement of the locomotive should therefore be of a character which will allow of both a wide and a deep firebox to be fitted.

Combustion Chamber. In order to ensure the most complete combustion of the fuel in the firebox so that it burns to CO_2 before the gases pass out

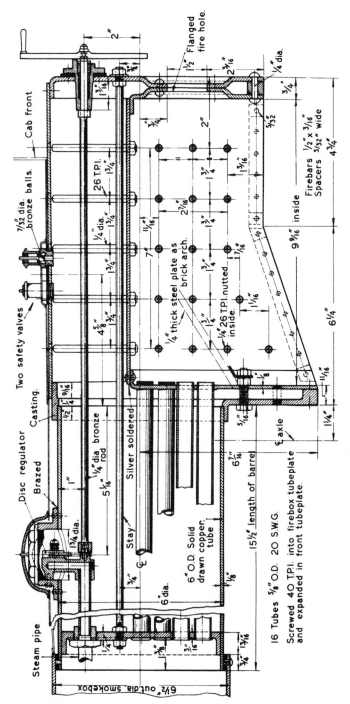

Fig. 15. 5-inch Gauge Locomotive-type Boiler

of the flue-tubes, an extended chamber is sometimes fitted at the firebox end. The flue-tubes are thereby shortened, and in real practice this is often an advantage where boilers are of great length and the tubes have a long, unsupported span between tube plates. As early as 1903, Greenly designed a boiler with an extended large flue from the firebox with a series of cross water-tubes in it. In modern design it is necessary to provide one or more large flue-tubes for the steam superheater pipes in addition to the small tubes surrounding them. These large tubes provide to some degree a space for combustion in addition to the space above the arched baffle plate in the firebox. This baffle plate (brick-arch) is made of mild steel plate— ¼-inch thick for 5-inch gauge—and is simply supported, not fixed in any way, on suitable studs at the side of the firebox. It should be made easily removable so that it can be replaced by a new plate (Fig. 15).

Safety Valve. This is the most important fitting on a boiler. No matter how small the model or how low the pressure, it is important to see that this valve is in proper working order and that it 'blows off' at the correct pressure for which the boiler is designed. It must be of the correct capacity, otherwise if too small it is possible to generate steam to a pressure in excess of the 'blow-off' pressure. For large models two safety valves are usually placed side by side and set to blow off together. They should be examined regularly.

CHAPTER IV

HANDLING MODEL LOCOMOTIVES

Testing the Boiler

PRESUMING that construction is completed and from an inspection everything is in order, the next procedure is to test the boiler under water and steam pressure. The boiler must be steam-tight—that is a *sine qua non*—independent of its ability to safely withstand the working pressure. Therefore, test it for leaks; minute leaks being marked and stopped up afterwards. The method of eliminating such minor leaks will depend on the size of the boiler and the particular construction involved. Soft soldering is the usual procedure, but would not be used for water-tube boilers or water-tubes of any sort.

The water test should be about 50% above the maximum working pressure, and for a steam test, the limiting figure is about 20% above the working pressure. For all tests under steam the safety valve must be in place and working. It is recommended that boilers should initially be given thorough hydraulic and steam tests by a competent engineer and then at regular intervals during the service of the locomotives.

Testing the Engine

In this case the presumption is that the whole mechanism is completely erected and moves freely when turned by hand. Then the valve timing must be set correctly according to the design of the model. To test it for working as a preliminary, air pressure may be employed, supplied from a motor-tyre pump with receiver.

By using air, valve functions may be checked over without burning the fingers in the processes of adjustment.

Raising Steam

The steam test involves the lighting of the fire—lamp or solid fuel—and in going over this the proper combustion must be obtained. With a spirit lamp burning under natural draught, there is nothing more to do than to trim it and light it and wait for sufficient steam to run the model. Never be too anxious to start the engine, always get a good head of steam pressure before opening the regulator. Do this for a few moments to warm the cylinders and then let the pressure rise again before commencing the run.

With an internally-fired boiler the question of providing an auxiliary draught before the steam is raised to an extent sufficient to work the engine or to apply the blower only must be carefully considered. Auxiliary blowers are used for this purpose. One form is a hand pump coupled to a small jet not bigger than $\frac{1}{32}$ inch for small models.

This jet is placed pointing upwards in a piece of tube which can fit into and form an extension to the locomotive chimney. For both large and small models much time will be saved if the auxiliary extension blower is worked by steam. A model stationary boiler is recommended for this purpose complete with pressure gauge and safety valve. The amount of water to be evaporated in the auxiliary steam-raising boiler will depend on the size of the model and the length of time required to get enough steam to work the blower. A twelve-minute run is the average for a $2\frac{1}{2}$-inch gauge model.

A vacuum cleaner which is provided with a means of blowing air, as well as drawing it through the fan, is also a useful device for steam raising. An induction blower with extension funnel opened out to about 2-inch diameter with a large, say, $\frac{1}{2}$-inch diameter, upturned air jet in it, may be rigged up.

For coal-fired boilers, charcoal can be used at the outset. This material burns easily and is clean. Coal when used with the moderate draught the auxiliary blower provides is liable to choke the flue-tubes. Where air pressure is obtainable, steam raising may be accomplished by connecting the pump to the boiler and using the ordinary blower with which the engine is fitted until such time as the steam pressure is higher than the air pressure.

Accessories

Among the many useful accessories that are now to be added to working model locomotives may be mentioned: (1) axle-driven pumps fitted with by-pass valves to return excess feed water to the tanks; (2) concealed whistles to give a reasonable note, a scale whistle being an impossible acoustic instrument; (3) injectors for boiler feeding of larger models; and

(4) air brakes operating on both the engine and the train. For large models with plenty of steaming capacity, steam-operated brakes controlled by a specially designed driver's valve in the cab are recommended.

Brakes

In real practice provision is made for braking the locomotive, tender, and the following train. All the vehicles are under the control of the driver—with certain exceptions where automatic train-control is operative in emergencies. For very small models brakes are not required to work, but can of course be made true to scale and fitted to the engine for the sake of completeness in design. For large models carrying the driver and a number of passengers, brakes are essential and should be sufficiently robust and perhaps slightly over scale if they are to be effective in bringing the train to a standstill when desired.

Steam-operated brakes are usually fitted to the locomotive driving and coupled wheels and hand-operated brakes for the tender. Vacuum brakes of the simple system are sometimes fitted to $10\frac{1}{4}$-inch gauge models. In the case of 15-inch gauge public miniature railways the regulation vacuum brake system or that of the compressed-air system is obligatory throughout the train.

For the 5- and $7\frac{1}{4}$-inch gauges the compensated brake system of levers is recommended. This method ensures an equal distribution of the load on all coupled wheels (or tender wheels) when braking.

At speed, brakes can be applied 'full-on' and then gradually pulled off as the speed slackens.

CHAPTER V

DESIGNS FOR NO. 0 AND NO. 1 GAUGE LOCOMOTIVES

THE No. 0 gauge model railway is becoming increasingly popular as an outdoor system, and opportunities to run actual working model steam locomotives are therefore more numerous; the indoor steam railway is not always popular with the domestic authority!

A simple type of locomotive in No. 0 gauge is specified in this chapter for the benefit of the beginner—all other designs being set out for No. 1 gauge. The first design can, of course, be enlarged to suit No. 1 gauge if desired, or the larger models scaled down to No. 0 gauge in the proportion of 10 to 7 for all external features, although internally certain modifications are usually found to be necessary if the engine is to work satisfactorily.

The British Railway Modelling Standards Bureau, under the chairmanship of Mr. J. N. Maskelyne, A.I.Loco.E., has introduced standard dimensions for rails, track, buffers, wheels, and axles, etc., for all gauges up to and including No. 1. Readers are recommended to adopt the standards for their railway, locomotives, and rolling stock.

DESIGN NO. 1. 0–4–4 TANK LOCOMOTIVE

No. 0 Gauge. Scale: 7 mm. to the foot

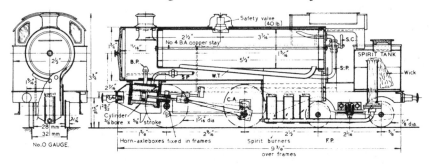

Fig. 16. 0-4-4 Tank Locomotive

Specification

This is a simple spirit-fired model suitable for the beginner in model making. It is fitted with a single inside cylinder and a simple reversing gear (Fig. 16).

Coupled Wheels. 36-mm. diameter ($1\frac{7}{16}$ inches) on the tread.

Trailing Wheels. 21-mm. diameter on the tread ($\frac{7}{8}$ inch). The axles should be arranged with a maximum side play of $\frac{1}{4}$ inch to allow the engine to run round curves.

Cylinder. One inside cylinder of the double-acting slide valve pattern, $\frac{3}{8}$-inch diameter by $\frac{5}{8}$-inch stroke. The machinery to be set out as in Fig. 3.

Boiler. Plain outside-fired copper boiler, $1\frac{3}{8}$-inch diameter. Shell 24 s.w.g. thick. The ends of the boiler to be made from 16 s.w.g. flanged copper sheet. The steam supply to the cylinder to be controlled by a simple cock on the back plate. The safety valve is fitted under the dome and should be set to blow off at 40 lb. per square inch. Boiler to be thoroughly tested with water pressure to 60 lb. per square inch. No pump is required; the boiler is filled by hand.

Spirit Burner. A three-wick (asbestos) spirit lamp to be fitted inside a flame guard. The spirit is contained in the rear bunker and fed to the burners by a siphon wick tube. The quantity of spirit should not exceed one-third that of the water in the boiler.

Lubricator. The cylinder is supplied with oil by means of an oil cup with a steam-tight screw cap below the footplate.

Tractive Effort. 1·3 lb.

DESIGN NO. 2. A SIMPLE WORKING MODEL 2–4–2 TANK LOCOMOTIVE

No. 1 Gauge (1¾ inches). Scale: 10 mm. to the foot

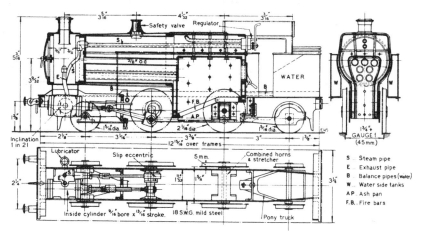

Fig. 17. Model 2-4-2 type Tank Locomotive

Specification

This type of tank locomotive was employed for passenger working on the G.W.R. (3600 class).

For this simple model, a single inside cylinder of the double-acting, slide valve pattern is fitted. Bore $\frac{9}{16}$ by $1\frac{3}{16}$-inch stroke (Fig. 17).

Coupled Wheels. 2 $\frac{1}{16}$-inch diameter fitted to $\frac{5}{16}$-inch diameter axles ($\frac{1}{4}$-inch diameter in the wheels). The wheels to run in standard sprung axleboxes with cast gun-metal horns bolted to the main frames.

Pony Trucks. (Front and rear.) The wheels are 1 $\frac{5}{16}$ inches on the tread and fitted in swivelling and sprung cast frames. (Movement of front truck restricted.)

Main Frames. No. 18 gauge steel plate with standard cast gun-metal buffer beams front and rear.

Boiler. A standard locomotive coal-fired type with 2 $\frac{3}{16}$-inch diameter barrel of 20-gauge copper tube. All the tube plates are flanged. Seven $\frac{5}{16}$-inch outside diameter copper fire-tubes in 22 or 24 gauge are fitted between the tube plates. All joints to be silver soldered. The outside casing or cleading is tapered in the usual G.W.R. style. The firebox is of the orthodox Belpaire pattern.

Fittings. 'Pop' safety valve (Bond's) to blow off at 50 lb. per square inch., plug-cock regulator, water gauge, check valve, lever-type hand pump fitted in one of the side tanks.

Fuel. Soft Welsh anthracite.

Water Feed. The feed water can be carried in the two side tanks. The tanks must be cross-connected by a $\frac{5}{16}$-inch pipe. Fill with rain water (filtered).

Tractive Effort. 3 lb.

DESIGN NO. 3. 4-4-0 TYPE EXPRESS ENGINE
(L.M.S.R.)

No. 1 Gauge (1¾ inches). Scale: 10 mm. to the foot

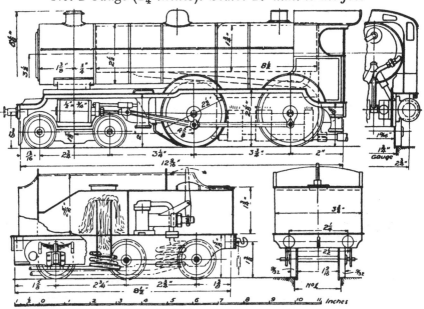

Fig. 18. L.M.S.R. 4-4-0 Locomotive

The model is based upon the well-known 'Midland Compounds' of the old Midland Railway and L.M.S.R.

Specification

Cylinders. Two outside cylinders (non-compound) with valve chests inside the frames; ½-inch bore by ¾-inch stroke.

Valve Gear. Slip eccentric type (see Fig. 4).

Wheels. Coupled wheels, 2½-inch diameter. Bogie wheels 1$\frac{3}{16}$-inch diameter and the tender wheels 1⅜-inch diameter.

Tractive Effort. 4 lb.

Main Frames. No. 18 gauge, bright mild steel plate with cast gun-metal buffer planks.

Bogie. Standard bogie, sprung and equalized.

Boiler. Smithies internally fired type, with 2½-inch diameter outer sheet steel (Belpaire form), and $1\frac{3}{4}$-inch inner boiler with three $\frac{7}{32}$-inch water-tubes. General construction similar to boiler (Fig. 13).

Spirit Burner. Two $\frac{5}{8}$-inch diameter wick tubes and one $\frac{3}{4}$- by $\frac{3}{8}$-inch oval tube behind driving axle. Induced draught on fire. Spirit reservoir in tender with coil feed pipe and siphon feed.

Tender. Six-wheeled type; centre axle to have $\frac{1}{8}$-inch side play. Steel frames $2\frac{1}{2}$ inches wide over outside face.

Water Feed Arrangements. Hand pump, lever type, submerged in rear water compartment of tender tanks. Delivery with coiled feed pipe to check valve on back of boiler.

Regulator. Standard back plate type or smokebox type with combined steam blower for producing draught while engine is standing. Bassett-Lowke regulator with separate blower valve.

Superheater. Return-tube through firebox type.

DESIGN NO. 4. SOUTHERN REGION 'SCHOOLS' CLASS EXPRESS LOCOMOTIVE

No. 1 Gauge ($1\frac{3}{4}$ inches). Scale: 10 mm. to the foot

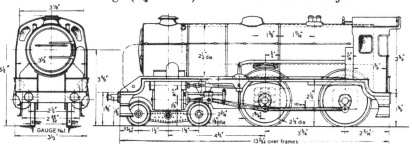

Fig. 19. S.R. 'Schools' Class Locomotive

Specification

Engine Type. 4–4–0 type wheel arrangement, express passenger locomotive based on the famous 'Schools' class of the Southern Railway (No. 900 'Eton', etc.).

Cylinders (2). Outside cylinders with piston-valve type slide valves on top and all outside motion. Cylinders $\frac{7}{16}$-inch bore by 20-mm. ($1\frac{13}{16}$-inch) stroke.

Valve Gear. Reversing valve motion of the Greenly-Joy type similar in details to the gear illustrated in design (Fig. 5). Reversing lever on left-hand side. Alternatively, Walschaerts' gear can be employed.

Main Frames. Bright mild steel, planished, No. 18 s.w.g. in thickness, fitted into cast gun-metal buffer planks.

Bogie. Standard $2\frac{3}{4}$-inch wheelbase or special Southern Railway type with 3-inch wheelbase. Cast in gun-metal.

Coupled Wheels. $2\frac{1}{2}$-inch diameter on tread, cast iron on $\frac{5}{16}$-inch diameter sprung axles.

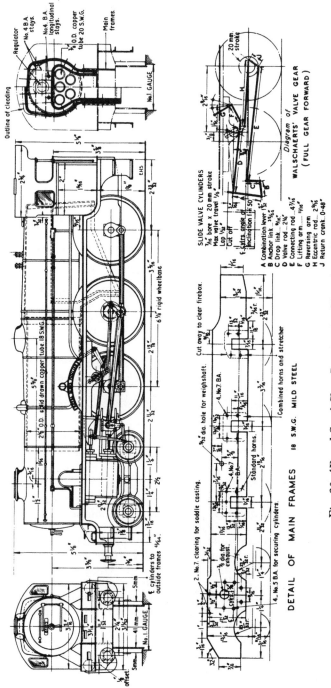

Fig. 20. 'Royal Scot' Class Locomotive No. 46103 (L.M.R. type)

Bogie Wheels. 1$\frac{3}{16}$-inch diameter on tread, cast iron.

Tender Wheels. 1$\frac{3}{8}$-inch diameter on tread, cast iron.

Boiler (a) Water-tube type with three $\frac{1}{4}$-inch diameter water-tubes.

(*b*) Alternatively loco-type boiler with deep, narrow firebox (see Fig. 17).

Regulator. Combined steam and blower type in smokebox. Steam taken from filler under dome. Twin steam pipes one to each cylinder.

Superheater. Bent back type of $\frac{3}{16}$-inch copper tube in duplicate, one for each cylinder. (To pass over flames of burners.)

Spirit Burner. Four rectangular wick tubes $\frac{3}{8}$ by $\frac{5}{8}$ inch. Asbestos yarn wicks.

Spirit Feed. Reservoir in tender with float feed or siphon wick as for previous design (Fig. 19).

Water Feed. Water supply carried in rear half of tender, with lever hand pump. Flexible connections to engine. Check valve and water gauge.

DESIGN NO. 5. WORKING MODEL 'ROYAL SCOT' CLASS LOCOMOTIVE (L.M.R.)
No. 1 Gauge

Specification

Engine Type. Modern three-cylinder outside motion type with 4–6–0 wheel arrangement, as used on main-line railways.

Cylinders. 'Piston valve' type, valves above, fitted with slide valves and interchangeable with the S.R. 'Schools'. $\frac{7}{16}$-inch diameter by 20-mm. stroke. Cylinders inclined to driving axle. (Only two cylinders need be fitted.)

Valve Gear. All outside valve motion of the Walschaerts' design, arranged as detailed in drawing (Fig. 5).

Driving Wheels. Six-coupled, standard 2$\frac{5}{8}$-inch diameter cast iron on $\frac{5}{16}$-inch plain axles shouldered down to $\frac{1}{4}$ inch in wheels. All coupled axles in sprung axle-boxes and cast gun-metal horns.

Bogie. L.M.S. type with 2$\frac{1}{2}$-inch wheelbase, sprung and equalized cast-iron wheels 1$\frac{3}{16}$-inch diameter on tread.

Frames. 18 s.w.g. steel plate fitted with cast gun-metal buffer beams.

Boiler. For this locomotive the orthodox type of coal-fired boiler is employed. The barrel is made of solid-drawn copper tube 2$\frac{1}{8}$-inch outside diameter. The firebox is fitted behind the middle driving axle and slopes upwards and over the rear axle. The flue gases from the firebox pass along five $\frac{3}{8}$-inch outside diameter copper tubes to the smokebox. All joints to be silver soldered.

Water Feed. Water is taken from the tender along a feed pipe to the axle-driven pump situated between the frames of the engine, thence to the boiler via a check valve. A by-pass pipe with valve provides for the return of water to the tender when not required to fill the boiler. A hand-feed pump is also fitted in the tender and connected to the boiler-feed system.

Tractive Effort. 3$\frac{1}{2}$ lb.

DESIGN NO. 6. AMERICAN 'PACIFIC'. TYPE LOCOMOTIVE

No. 1 Gauge.   Scale: 10 mm. to the foot

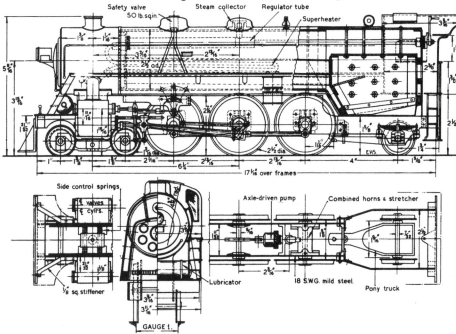

Fig. 21. American 'Pacific' Locomotive

This engine is designed to suit the larger loading gauge which is standard in the U.S.A. and Canada. The scale equivalent is $102\frac{1}{2}$-mm. wide by 150-mm. high.

Specification

Cylinders. There are two outside cylinders only, $\frac{1}{2}$-inch bore by 20-mm. stroke. (Slide valves.)

Valve Gear. For this model the Baker gear is shown. It is a variant of the well-known Walschaerts' gear in so far as a special system of levers is employed in place of the radius rod and expansion link.

Main Frames. No. 18 s.w.g. steel. (Note that the rear portion is designed to clear trailing truck and firebox.)

Boiler. This is the locomotive coal-fired type with wide firebox. There are six $\frac{3}{8}$-inch outside diameter fire-tubes and one large fire-tube to take the spearhead superheater. The main barrel is $2\frac{1}{2}$-inch outside diameter by 14 s.w.g. thick. Working pressure 60 lb. per square inch. The total evaporative heating surface is 108 square inches. The H.S. to grate area ratio is 26·8–1.

Safety Valve. To blow off at a pressure not exceeding 1 to 2 lb. above the stated maximum. The aperture under the valve to be $\frac{3}{16}$-inch diameter.

Bogie. The bogie to be equalized, sprung, and fitted with side control springs.

Tractive Effort. 5 lb.

DESIGN NO. 7. WORKING MODEL DOUBLE BOGIE EXPRESS TANK LOCOMOTIVE

(4–4–4 or 4–6–4)

No. 1 Gauge

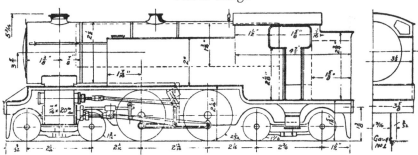

Fig. 22. Tank Locomotive designed for Sharp Curves

Specification

Engine Type. 4–4–4 tank locomotive. This design can be made up out of standard parts used for tender locomotives of the 'Atlantic' or 'Pacific' type. As drawn the engine is to be well recommended for any line which has sharp curves. The two bogies are identical in design. Where the extra length of the engine is not objected to, six-coupled wheels may be employed, making the locomotive into a 4–6–4 or 'Baltic' tank engine.

Cylinders. 'Piston valve' type, but with slide valves fitted, $\frac{7}{16}$-inch diameter by 20-mm. stroke.

Valve Gear. Valves driven by all outside motion of the Greenly type as detailed in Chapter II or Walschaerts' gear may be employed.

Bogies. Any standard design with sprung and equalized side frames and $1\frac{3}{16}$-inch diameter cast-iron wheels.

Driving Wheels. The coupled wheels are $2\frac{3}{32}$-inch diameter.

Boiler. Water-tube type with $2\frac{1}{2}$-inch diameter outer shell, round-topped firebox and inner boiler $1\frac{3}{4}$-inch diameter. Three $\frac{7}{32}$-inch water-tubes. A twin pipe superheater to pass over the burners.

Spirit Tank. The reservoir for methylated spirit is carried in the back bunker and the fuel fed to the burners with a wick siphon as in design (Fig. 18).

Feed Water. The side tanks to be made to hold water and one of them to

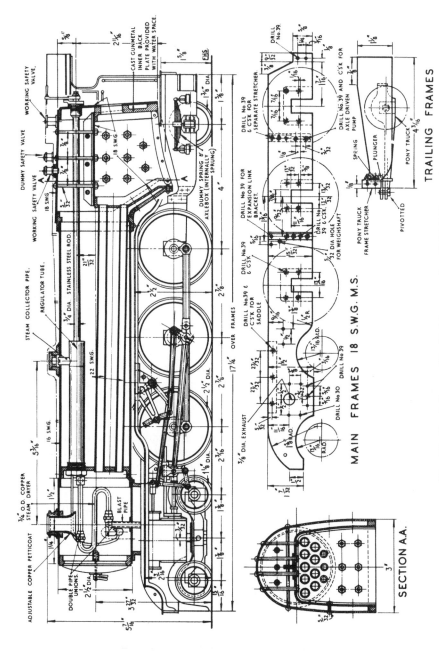

Fig. 23. No. 1 Gauge 'Pacific' Locomotive (L.N.E.R. type)

carry a hand pump. Tanks to be cross-connected by a $\frac{5}{16}$-inch diameter pipe to equalize the water levels.

Tractive Effort. $3\frac{3}{4}$ lb.

DESIGN NO. 8. NO. 1 GAUGE 'PACIFIC' LOCOMOTIVE (L.N.E.R. TYPE)

Scale 10 mm.

This is one of the most popular types of locomotives for modelling in any gauge up to and including 15 inches and is particularly suitable for No. 1 gauge. Working drawings of the model have been prepared by Elenora H. Steel with a view to employing standard castings throughout.

Specification

Cylinders. Two outside only. 'Piston valve' type fitted with slide valves. $\frac{1}{2}$-inch bore by 20-mm. stroke.

Valve Gear. Walschaerts' modified to suit slide-valve cylinders. For this gear to function efficiently, the standard of workmanship must be good. (See *Walschaerts' Valve Gear* by H. Greenly—P. Marshall & Co. Ltd.)

Bogie. Standard Greenly No. 1 gauge design, equalized and fitted with side control springs. $1\frac{1}{8}$-inch diameter wheels.

Trailing Truck. In place of the radial axle-box, a standard No. 1 gauge spring-loaded truck is fitted. Wheels $1\frac{3}{8}$-inch diameter.

Driving Wheels. Standard pattern, $2\frac{1}{2}$-inch diameter.

Boiler. Locomotive type. Coal-fired with wide firebox. Nine $\frac{1}{4}$-inch diameter fire-tubes. Steam dryer in smokebox. Semi-rotary disc regulator with blower valve combined. Barrell $2\frac{1}{4}$-inch diameter (16 s.w.g.).

Boiler Feed. Axle-driven pump, by-pass valve and check valve with feed pipes from tender. A submerged hand pump may be fitted in tender.

Tractive Effort. $4\frac{1}{2}$ lb.

CHAPTER VI

DESIGNS FOR $2\frac{1}{2}$- AND $3\frac{1}{2}$-INCH GAUGE LOCOMOTIVES

The $\frac{1}{2}$-inch scale (or more correctly the $\frac{17}{32}$-inch or 14-mm. scale) and the $\frac{3}{4}$-inch scale represent the middle course for model makers to take when in doubt as to the size they should choose. In many cases 5-inch gauge is too large for the small workshop, and machine tools just that much too light to take heavy castings. On the other hand, the degree of accuracy required to construct a successful working model in No. 0 gauge may be alien to the temperament of the builder. He therefore decides upon either $2\frac{1}{2}$- or $3\frac{1}{2}$-inch gauge—the bias to-day being usually with the latter size.

DESIGN NO. 9. WORKING MODEL EXPRESS LOCOMOTIVE 'LORD NELSON' (S.R.)

2½-inch Gauge. Scale: $\frac{17}{32}$ inch to the foot

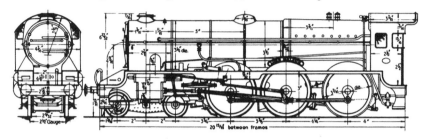

Fig. 24. 'Lord Nelson' Express Locomotive

The 'Lord Nelson' class (4–6–0) was designed by Mr. R. E. L. Maunsell, chief mechanical engineer of the Southern Railway in 1926 for heavy passenger train working. It has four cylinders and four sets of Walschaerts' gear, whereas this small model is fitted with the two outside cylinders only.

Specification

Cylinders. $\frac{11}{16}$-inch bore by $1\frac{1}{16}$-inch stroke. Piston or slide valves can be fitted. Piston-valve cylinders are shown in Fig. 24, so that, if slide valves are to be employed, it will be necessary to modify the combination lever and return crank. (See Fig. 28.)

Coupled Wheels. $3\frac{7}{16}$-inch diameter on $\frac{3}{8}$-inch diameter steel axles, fitted into sprung axle-boxes working in gun-metal horn-blocks.

Bogie Wheels. $1\frac{5}{8}$-inch diameter. Tender wheels. $1\frac{7}{8}$-inch diameter.

Bogie. Equalized and the four wheels mounted in sprung axle-boxes.

Main Loco Frames. $\frac{1}{16}$-inch bright steel plate, 2 inches apart.

Boiler. Locomotive-type boiler with six $\frac{3}{8}$-inch fire-tubes and one $\frac{5}{8}$-inch fire-tube to take superheater element. Barrel $3\frac{1}{4}$-inch diameter. Stays $\frac{3}{16}$-inch diameter copper (40 t.p.i.) pitched at $\frac{7}{8}$-inch centres.

Boiler Feed. Hand pump in the tender and axle-driven pump on the locomotive.

Lubrication. For the cylinders steam or water displacement oiling system fitted between the locomotive frames.

Tractive Effort. $8\frac{3}{4}$ lb.

DESIGN NO. 10. MODEL SIX-COUPLED GOODS LOCOMOTIVE

North British Railway

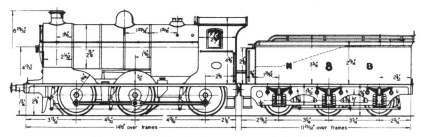

Fig. 25. 0-6-0 Goods Locomotive of the N.B.R.

Specification

Engine Type. This is a standard British 0–6–0 Goods type of the old N.B.R. The design exemplifies one of the most successful type of locomotive used in these Isles. It is robust and simple as well as very symmetrical in external proportions.

Tractive Effort. 12 lb.

Cylinders. For a $2\frac{1}{2}$-inch gauge model the inside cylinders are $\frac{11}{16}$-inch bore by $1\frac{1}{16}$-inch stroke. (Slide valves on top of cylinders.)

Valve Gear. Indirect link motion with rocker arm.[1]

Coupled Wheels. $2\frac{5}{8}$-inch diameter.

Tender Wheels. 2-inch diameter.

Boiler. Locomotive type, coal-fired with five $\frac{7}{16}$-inch tubes.

Firebox. $1\frac{7}{8}$ inches wide by $4\frac{3}{4}$ inches long.

DESIGN NO. 11. 2–6–4 TANK LOCOMOTIVE

British Railways Class 4 Style

$2\frac{1}{2}$-inch Gauge. Scale: $\frac{17}{32}$ inch to the foot

The design (Fig. 26) exemplifies a type of tank engine introduced on British Railways in 1951 and is one recommended for modelling in $2\frac{1}{2}$-inch gauge or larger if desired. It is suitable for heavy duty on an outdoor model railway system. The weight on all six-coupled wheels should not be less than three-quarters of the total weight of the engine in working order. The tractive effort is 10 lb., and the engine is capable of hauling a load of 250 lb. on a level track.

The front and rear ends of the engine are guided by a swivelling bogie ___d pony truck respectively, and therefore the locomotive rides very well indeed on lines with sharp curves. The minimum radius recommended for $2\frac{1}{2}$-inch gauge is 10 feet (3 metres).

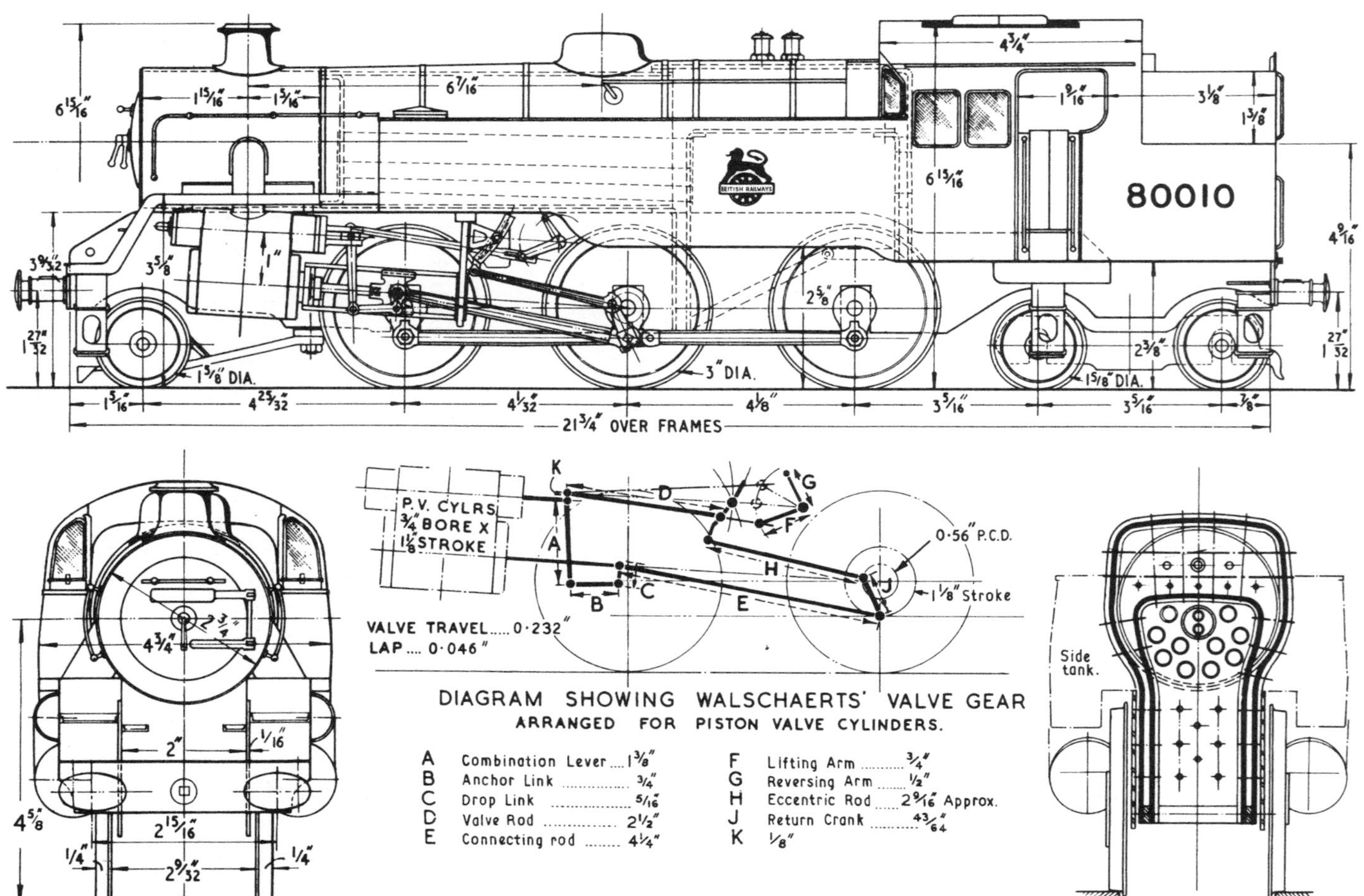
80010
BRITISH RAILWAYS
21 3/4" OVER FRAMES
1 5/8" DIA.
3" DIA.
15/8" DIA.
P.V. CYLRS
3/4" BORE X
1 1/8" STROKE
VALVE TRAVEL..... 0·232"
LAP.... 0·046"
0·56" P.C.D.
1 1/8" Stroke
DIAGRAM SHOWING WALSCHAERTS' VALVE GEAR
ARRANGED FOR PISTON VALVE CYLINDERS.
A Combination Lever.... 1 3/8"
B Anchor Link .... 3/4"
C Drop Link .... 5/16"
D Valve Rod .... 2 1/2"
E Connecting rod .... 4 1/4"
F Lifting Arm .... 3/4"
G Reversing Arm .... 1/2"
H Eccentric Rod ..... 2 9/16" Approx.
J Return Crank .... 43/64"
K 1/8"
Side tank.
2 1/2" GAUGE

Fig. 26. Model 2-6-4 type Tank Locomotive

Specification

Cylinders. $\frac{5}{8}$-inch bore by $1\frac{1}{8}$-inch stroke. Two outside cylinders only inclined on a slope of 1 in 16 with the valve chests on top. Piston-valve or slide-valve cylinders may be fitted.

Valve Gear. Outside Walschaerts' designed to give a maximum cut-off of 85% of the stroke.

Slide Valves. Steam port opening 0·07 by $\frac{1}{4}$ inch wide. Exhaust port opening 0·14 by $\frac{1}{4}$ inch wide. Thickness of port bar 0·08 inch. Lap of valve 0·046 inch. Total valve travel 0·232 inch.

Coupled Wheels. 3-inch diameter on the tread and of a good close-grained cast iron. Wheels to be an even press fit on ground steel axles and keyed. The right-hand crank-pins to be a quarter turn in advance of the left-hand crank-pin (90°). The axles to be $\frac{3}{8}$-inch diameter and carried in gun-metal axle-boxes on underhung coil springs.

Bogie. As the trailing end of the engine overhangs the track a considerable amount when negotiating a sharp curve, the slot in the bogie stretcher must be wide enough to allow side play of the central pin. Allow for a total movement of $\frac{3}{8}$ inch. The bogie to be equalized and sprung. Wheels $1\frac{19}{32}$-inch diameter.

Pony Truck. The wheels are $1\frac{19}{32}$-inch diameter. The truck is sprung and pivoted at a point $3\frac{1}{4}$ inches behind the axle.

Boiler. Locomotive type with narrow firebox. It may be designed and tested for a working pressure of 65 lb. per square inch on the gauge.

DESIGN NO. 12. CALEDONIAN EXPRESS 4–4–0 LOCOMOTIVE NO. 114. CALEDONIAN RAILWAY

$3\frac{1}{2}$-inch Gauge. Scale: $\frac{3}{4}$ inch to the foot

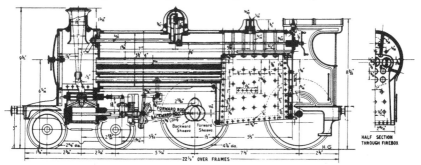

Fig. 27. Caledonian Express Locomotive

In 1916 Mr. William Pickersgill, locomotive superintendent of the Caledonian Railway, introduced a 4–4–0 superheater passenger loco-motive of unusually large dimensions. The two inside cylinders were 20-inch diameter by 26-inch stroke. The lubricator was driven from a small return-crank on the right-hand leading coupling-rod pin. No. 114 was built at the St. Rollox Works, Glasgow.

The engine is an excellent type to model in ¾-inch scale (one-sixteenth full-size) where skill in boiler making, valve gear construction, and the setting out of the chassis can be practised (Fig. 27).

Specification

Cylinders. Two inside, $1\frac{3}{16}$-inch bore by $1\frac{5}{8}$-inch stroke. Slide valves on top.
Valve Gear. Stephenson's (indirect) motion. The valve rod is operated through a one-to-one rocker arm.
Coupled Wheels. $4\frac{7}{8}$-inch diameter.
Bogie Wheels. $2\frac{5}{8}$-inch diameter.
Tender Wheels. 3-inch diameter.
Boiler. Barrel $3\frac{3}{4}$-inch outside diameter. Material: copper. Rotary disc-type regulator fitted inside dome.
Superheater. Fire-tube type. The boiler is fitted with three large flue-tubes to take one superheater element in each. The elements are connected to inlet and outlet headers to cylinders.
Tractive Effort. 21 lb. Hauling load 450 lb.

DESIGN NO. 13. 'PACIFIC' TYPE LOCOMOTIVE (L.N.E.R.)

$3\frac{1}{2}$-inch Gauge. Scale: ¾ inch to the foot

Of the many locomotives designed and built for $3\frac{1}{2}$-inch gauge rail-ways, the L.N.E.R. 'Pacific' is undoubtedly one of the most popular among model makers ever since Sir Nigel Gresley introduced the famous 'Great Northern' (No. 1470 of the G.N.R.) in 1922. Three cylinders can be fitted and provision made for compounding if desired. (Walschaerts' gear and the special conjugated link motion for the inside cylinder.) The latter arrangement can be adapted for $1\frac{1}{2}$-inch scale working models to better advantage. The model locomotive under consideration is designed for two outside cylinders only (Fig. 28).

Specification

Cylinders. (Two) slide valve type, 1-inch bore by $1\frac{5}{8}$-inch stroke. Alternatively piston valve cylinders can be fitted.
Pump. Boiler feed pump fitted to stretcher between frames. Driven by eccentric on rear coupled axle. Stroke ¾ inch.
Coupled Wheels. $4\frac{7}{8}$-inch diameter.
Bogie Wheels. $2\frac{1}{4}$-inch diameter.
Trailing Wheels. $2\frac{3}{4}$-inch diameter.
Tender Wheels. $3\frac{1}{8}$-inch diameter.
Boiler. Barrel $4\frac{1}{4}$-inch diameter, 15 inches long. Material: copper.
Pressure. 70 lb. per square inch.
Tractive Effort. 21 lb.
Main Frames. ⅛ inch thick (maximum), $3\frac{1}{2}$ inches wide.

The trailing axle is mounted on radial axle-boxes with free transverse movement in the horns. The rear frames are specially designed to take the wide firebox.

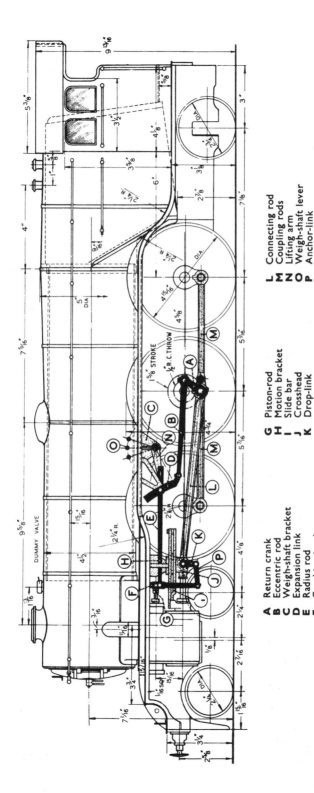

Fig. 28. L.N.E.R. 'Pacific' Locomotive showing the arrangement of Walschaerts' Valve Gear for Slide Valve Cylinders

A Return crank
B Eccentric rod
C Weigh-shaft bracket
D Expansion link
E Radius rod
F Combination lever

G Piston-rod
H Motion bracket
I Slide bar
J Crosshead
K Drop-link

L Connecting rod
M Coupling rods
N Lifting arm
O Weigh-shaft lever
P Anchor-link

Note. For the three-cylinder arrangement, the cranks are set at 120°, but since the inside cylinder is inclined the inside crank axle must be retarded by an amount equal to the angle of inclination. The angle is about 7°. For a two-cylinder scheme they are set at 90° with the right-hand crank in advance.

CHAPTER VII

PASSENGER-HAULING LOCOMOTIVES

STRICTLY speaking, the 1-inch scale should be employed for the old $4\frac{3}{4}$-inch gauge, and the locomotive designs set out on the drawing-board accordingly, but the $4\frac{3}{4}$-inch gauge has been largely superseded by the more popular 5-inch gauge railway. The correct 'true-to-scale' for 5-inch gauge is $1\frac{1}{16}$ inches to the foot; the author finds, however, that 1·1 inch or 28 mm. to the foot is a more practical size for locomotives with outside piston-valve cylinders.

While a lot of enjoyment can be obtained in demonstrating the passenger-hauling capabilities of $3\frac{1}{2}$-inch and even $2\frac{1}{2}$-inch gauge model locomotives on specially elevated tracks, the capacity of 5-inch engines brings them, if not within, at least on the border-line of 'miniature' systems which extend to the Lilliputian giants of one-third size scale, 15-inch gauge railways exemplified by the Fairbourne (Barmouth), Ravenglass and Eskdale, and the Romney Hythe and Dymchurch—to name but three well-known systems in Britain.

1·1-inch scale is approximately one-eleventh full-size, so that by employing an approximation of the 'cube law', a 'Pacific' type locomotive weighs about 3 cwt.

DESIGN NO. 14. 'KING ARTHUR' CLASS 4-6-0 LOCOMOTIVE (S.R.)

Scale: 1·1 *inch to the foot*

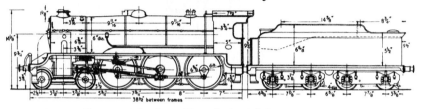

Fig. 29. Passenger-hauling 'King Arthur' S.R. Express Locomotive

Specification

Engine Type. Express tender locomotive with outside cylinders and valve gear (Fig. 29).

Cylinders. Two outside only. $1\frac{7}{16}$-inch bore by $2\frac{1}{4}$-inch stroke. $\frac{7}{8}$-inch piston valves. Materials: cast-iron cylinders and liners. Steel piston valves with cast iron or steel rings. Cast-iron pistons and rings.

Valve Gear. Fully corrected Greenly valve motion or Walschaerts' gear.

Boiler. Copper boiler, 6-inch diameter barrel, and narrow round-topped firebox. Firebox $3\frac{5}{16}$ inches wide by 11 inches long at foundation ring. Working pressure: 80 lb. per square inch (Fig. 15, p. 28).

Main Frames. $\frac{1}{8}$- or $\frac{5}{32}$-inch bright mild steel plate, with cast horn plates, gun-metal axle-boxes with helical springs.

Coupled and Driving Wheels. $6\frac{5}{8}$-inch diameter on $\frac{13}{16}$-inch diameter steel axles, cast iron. Balance weights cast to suit.

Tractive Effort. 50 lb. Hauling load: 14 cwt.

Bogie. Sprung and equalized bogie mounted on four $3\frac{1}{2}$-inch diameter wheels on $\frac{5}{8}$-inch diameter steel axles. Gun-metal axle-boxes.

Tender. Six-wheeled or bogie tender, preferably the latter.

Boiler Feed. Water carried in tender with connections to an axle-driven pump on the engine and a Bassett-Lowke automatic injector.

Note. The design of this locomotive can be employed for $2\frac{1}{2}$-inch gauge (14 mm. to the foot scale).

DESIGN NO. 15. 2-8-0 'AUSTERITY' LOCOMOTIVE

5-inch Gauge. $\frac{1}{11}$ full size

This engine (Fig. 30), a product of the war, excited the interest of model engineers and as soon as conditions permitted model making in earnest, working models were soon under construction on the bench. For the 5-inch gauge it was realized that a number of standard parts and patterns could be used to some advantage. With its small wheels it was possible to design a really powerful passenger-hauling engine. The setting out shown in Fig. 30 was prepared by the author.

Specification

Cylinders. Piston-valve type. (Two outside only) $1\frac{1}{2}$-inch bore by $2\frac{1}{4}$-inch stroke.

Wheels. Coupled (special pattern) $5\frac{3}{16}$-inch diameter. Leading truck $3\frac{3}{8}$-inch diameter (disc-type). Tender $4\frac{1}{4}$-inch diameter.

Valve Gear. Walschaerts'.

Boiler. Copper boiler 6-inch diameter. Narrow firebox. Working pressure: 80 lb. per square inch.

Main Frames. $\frac{1}{8}$- or $\frac{5}{32}$-inch bright mild steel plate.

Pony Truck. Pivoted on a 7-inch radius, equalized and sprung.

Tractive Effort. 70 lb. The hauling capacity, starting on a level track, is estimated at 1 ton.

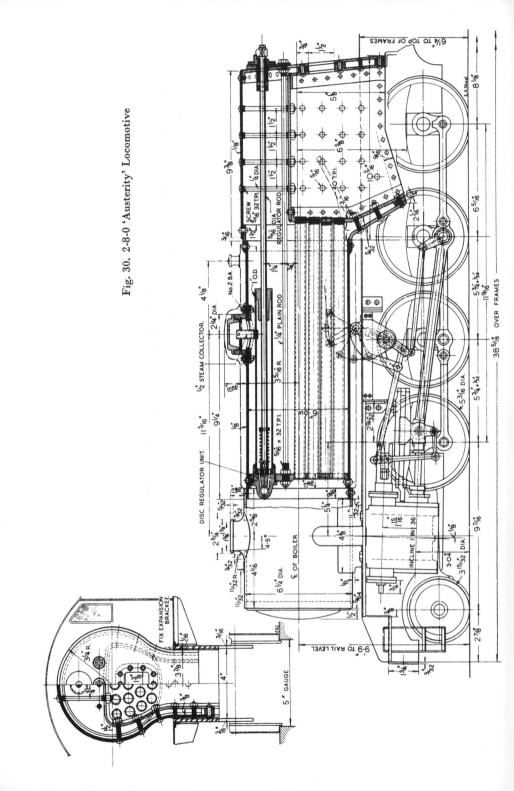

Fig. 30. 2-8-0 'Austerity' Locomotive

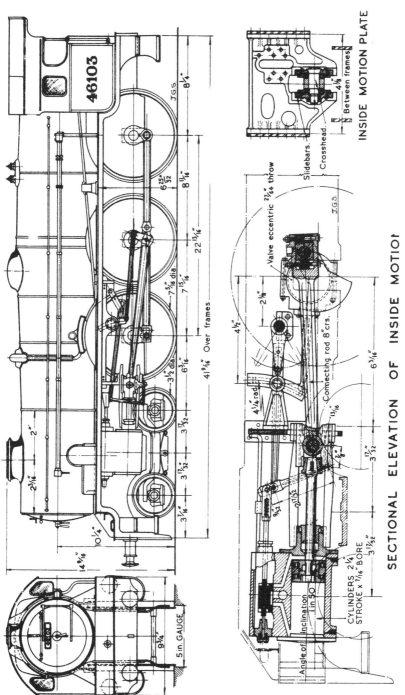

INSIDE MOTION PLATE

SECTIONAL ELEVATION OF INSIDE MOTION

Fig. 31. 'Royal Scot' Class Locomotive

DESIGN NO. 16. 'ROYAL SCOT' CLASS 4-6-0 LOCOMOTIVE L.M.R. (B.R.) No. 46103 'Royal Scots Fusilier'

5-inch Gauge. $\frac{1}{11}$ full size

The first 'Royal Scot' (L.M.S.R., No. 6100) was introduced by Sir Henry Fowler in 1927. The class had parallel boiler, and many models have been built in $3\frac{1}{2}$-inch and $7\frac{1}{4}$-inch gauges.[1] In 1943 the 'Royal Scots Fusilier' was rebuilt with a taper boiler and double chimney by Sir William Stanier. A working model can be designed with three cylinders and three sets of valve gear (Fig. 31). The working drawings for the model were prepared by John G. Steel. See also Fig. 6.

Specification

Cylinders. (Three) $1\frac{7}{16}$-inch bore by $2\frac{1}{4}$-inch stroke. The model is arranged for slide valves, but piston-valve cylinders can be fitted if required.

Valve Gear. Walschaerts' (inside and outside). The inside gear is driven by an eccentric mounted on the leading coupled axle. The setting out of the valve gear is for slide-valve cylinders.

Locomotive Wheels. Coupled $7\frac{5}{16}$-inch diameter. Bogie: $3\frac{1}{2}$-inch diameter.

Main Frames. $\frac{1}{8}$- or $\frac{5}{32}$-inch thick bright mild steel plate. $4\frac{3}{4}$ inches wide by 42 inches long.

Boiler. Taper boiler with superheater. Working pressure 85 lb. per square inch.

Tractive Effort. This is estimated at 55 lb. On a level track the engine is capable of hauling a load of $\frac{3}{4}$ ton from a standing start (say, ten or twelve adults).

Bogie. A load of 75 lb. distributed on the four wheels is transmitted through spring-loaded equalizers to the axle-boxes.

[1] The first $1\frac{1}{2}$-inch scale, $7\frac{1}{4}$-inch gauge model of the 'Royal Scot' was built by Bassett-Lowke Ltd. to working drawings by Henry Greenly. In 1938 a larger model ($10\frac{1}{4}$-inch gauge, $2\frac{1}{4}$ inches to the foot scale) was also constructed at Northampton.

DESIGN NO. 17. 'KING' CLASS 4-6-0 G.W.R.

$7\frac{1}{4}$-inch Gauge. $\frac{1}{8}$ full size

At Paddington Station, London, the traveller will not only have an opportunity to examine a full-size 'King' class locomotive about to start on its journey to the west of England, but, given the time, he will be able to scrutinize its replica in a glass case in the main concourse. The model, with its coach, is strictly to a scale of $1\frac{1}{2}$ inches to the foot, and was built by Mr. B. R. Hunt of Johannesburg.

The working steam model is designed with the four cylinders and inside Walschaerts' valve gear. (Working model drawings prepared by H. Greenly.)

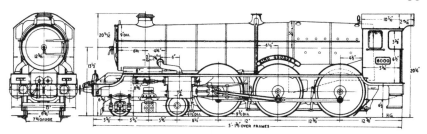

Fig. 32. 'Kings' Class 4-6-0 (G.W.R. Type)

Specification

Cylinders. (Four) $1\frac{3}{8}$-inch bore by $3\frac{1}{2}$-inch stroke. Piston valves.
Driving Wheels. $9\frac{3}{4}$-inch diameter.
Bogie Wheels. $4\frac{1}{4}$-inch diameter.
Length over rigid wheelbase, 2 feet $\frac{3}{8}$ inch.
Total length of locomotive over frames, 5 feet $1\frac{7}{8}$ inches.
Boiler (taper). Barrel $24\frac{1}{4}$ inches long by $8\frac{1}{2}$-inch diameter at the front tube plate; 25 tubes, $\frac{5}{8}$-inch diameter.
Working Pressure. 85 lb. per square inch.
Tractive Effort. 110 lb.
Tender Wheels. 6-inch diameter.
Valve Gear. Walschaerts'. Two sets of inside gear only with rocker arm transmission to outside cylinders (Fig. 33).
Safety Valve. Direct spring-loaded, $\frac{5}{8}$-inch diameter.
Cut-off. The piston valves are set to give a maximum cut-off of $78\frac{1}{2}\%$
Regulator. Slide valve pattern in smokebox and controlled from the cab.
Blast Manifold. Three-way pattern and fitted with a ring blower controlled by stop valve in cab.
Cab Fittings. Fittings for a working model comprise regulator handle, two valves for injectors, water gauge, pressure gauge, oiler for axle-boxes and reversing gear.
Loco Brakes. Steam or vacuum operated. All brakes compensated to ensure equal distribution of applied loads on each coupled wheel.
Water Pick-up. Provision is made to fit the water pick-up gear if desired. The minimum speed at which the apparatus will work is $7\frac{1}{2}$ m.p.h.

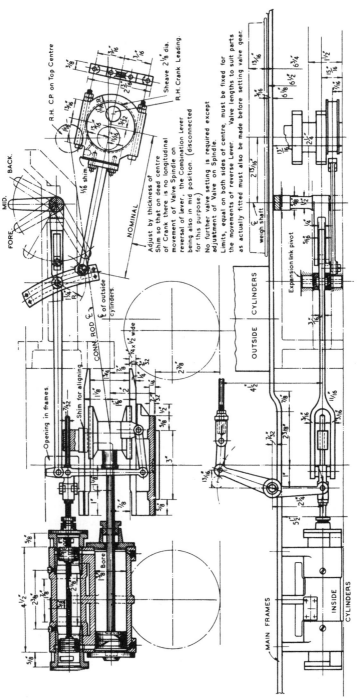

Fig. 33. Arrangement of Inside Walschaerts' Gear and Rocker Arm for Outside Cylinder. 1½-inch Scale Model of G.W.R. Locomotive

DESIGN NO. 18. THE 'RISBOROUGH' 4-6-4 TANK LOCOMOTIVE (FREE-LANCE DESIGN)

7¼-inch Gauge. Scale: 1½ inches to the foot

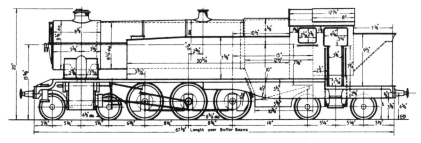

Fig. 34. Free-lance Tank Locomotive Design

This heavy-duty passenger locomotive is similar to Design No. 7 and is typical of Greenly's double-bogie engine designs. It can be conveniently fired by a driver seated on a suitable trailing wagon.

Specification

Tractive Effort. This is estimated at 135 lb. maximum. On a level track the engine should be capable of starting a load of 2 tons (32 adults).

Total Weight. 6½ cwt. (728 lb.). A weight of 570 lb. should be available for adhesion on the six coupled wheels.

Main Frames. To be made from $\frac{3}{16}$- by 6-inch bright steel plate. The outer (rear) frames can be made from the same material 3½ inch wide. Horns and stretchers may be cast or fabricated. Journals for coupled wheels to be 1⅛-inch diameter. Buffer beams 2¼- by ⅜-inch bright mild steel.

Wheels. To be cast in good quality grey cast iron. Coupled: 6⅝- or 6¾-inch diameter. Bogie: 4¼-inch diameter, eight required. Bogie axles (journals): $\frac{13}{16}$ inch or ⅞ inch.

Bogie. Load to be transmitted to axle-boxes through spring-loaded equalizers. Side control of bogie to be equally sprung. The rear bogie to be of similar construction and to carry a substructure forming part of main (rear) frames. Bogie may be fabricated and welded throughout, castings being used for the horns, axle-boxes, and centre pads only.

Boiler. The maximum working pressure need not exceed 90 lb. per square inch. It can be made in copper throughout or steel can be substituted if desired. The design of the main frames allows a wide firebox to be fitted.

Total evaporative heating surface 2000 square inches.

Grate area 63 square inches.

Ratio H.S. to G.A. = 32/1.

Type of regulator: Tubular with rotating diaphragm valve.
Size of flue-tubes: $\frac{5}{8}$-inch outside diameter.
Superheater tubes (two). $1\frac{1}{8}$-inch diameter.
Boiler feed: Axle-driven pump and one injector or two injectors only.

Cylinders. The bore should not exceed $2\frac{1}{4}$ inches. Stroke $3\frac{1}{4}$ inches. Two outside cylinders only are required. Greenly's double-ported piston-valve arrangement is recommended. Alternatively, slide-valve cylinders may be fitted. Cut-off not to be less then 83%. Material: cast iron.

Valve Gear. Outside Walschaerts'. Constant lead is provided and is available for the mid-gear position.

Note. This design may be adapted to suit $\frac{3}{4}$-inch scale, $3\frac{1}{2}$-inch gauge.

Side Tanks. These must be equalized by a balance pipe connecting one to the other. Inner tanks of copper prefabricated can be fitted inside the casing.

Lubricator. Wakefield type. (Axle-driven).

CHAPTER VIII

MINIATURE RAILWAY LOCOMOTIVES

Whilst the average model engineer is usually content to go no larger than $1\frac{1}{2}$-inch scale for passenger-hauling purposes, there are enthusiasts who are interested in the larger gauges ranging from $9\frac{1}{2}$ to 15 inches, and in some cases as large as 18 inches. One of the earliest 2-inch scale steam locomotives was an 'Atlantic' type based upon Henry A. Ivatt's famous G.N.R. locomotive No. 251 (Fig. 34). This model was built by Bassett-Lowke Ltd. to drawings prepared by Henry Greenly for Mr. J. E. P. Howey's railway in the grounds of Staughton Manor. This class of locomotive and the gauge is very popular, although the $10\frac{1}{4}$-inch gauge has now perhaps a greater following since the introduction of the $2\frac{1}{4}$-inch scale 'Royal Scot' in 1938. Larger and heavier locomotives of the 'Pacific' type have been built for this gauge and measured for a scale of $2\frac{1}{2}$ inches to the foot or one-fifth the size of the actual engines running on British Railways.

For these large scales and gauges, the 3 feet 6 inches Colonial standard with its larger loading gauge is often used for comparision and can be scaled down to advantage instead of having to base the scale on the 4 feet $8\frac{1}{2}$ inches British standard. Thus, when reduced to $10\frac{1}{4}$-inch gauge, a scale of 3 inches to the foot might well be employed to the better satisfaction of driver and passengers.

Greenly's original 15-inch gauge locomotive 'Little Giant', a 4–4–2 type built in 1904, was one-quarter the size of its full-size prototype. Another model 'Sans Pareil' of the same type was built to a scale of $3\frac{1}{4}$ inches to the foot in 1911, and it was just that much larger ($1\frac{1}{4}$ times by weight) to make it a more powerful machine (see design No. 19, p. 58). The tractive effort was 680 lb. compared with 380 lb. developed by the earlier engine. It was not until 1924 that he designed his 'Pacifics' one-third full-size for the Romney, Hythe, and Dymchurch Railway, a 15-inch gauge system in Kent. This scale is one that closely represents the Colonial standard in miniature, and it is possible to employ very powerful engines running at speeds over thirty miles per hour on a first-class track.

There are examples of 12-inch gauge railways extant on which loco-motives built to scales of 2½ and 3 inches are employed. It is a comfortable size from the passenger's point of view and a good substitute for the 15-inch line—particularly in cases where the terrain necessitates sharp curves.

For industrial purposes 18 inches is the minimum gauge recommended by railway engineers. By no stretch of the imagination, however, can such railways, as laid down in factories, mines, and plantations abroad, be classified as 'models' in the accepted sense since they are designed strictly for utilitarian purposes together with the larger-than-scale locomotives and rolling stock. As early as 1874 a 15-inch gauge railway was laid down at Duffield Bank near Derby for Sir Arthur P. Heywood. Although scale-model locomotives were not at that time employed—the line was opened for the conveyance of freight and passengers—the scheme encouraged others to promote similar miniature railways in England. A notable example was the very extensive system laid down in 1894 for the Duke of Westminster at Eaton Hall near Chester. The line from Balderton Station on the G.W.R. covered a distance of three miles directly to the Hall. There was also a network of branch lines which brought the total up to about four miles of track.

In the first decade of the century miniature railways were laid down in parks at Blackpool, Rhyl, Geneva, and elsewhere. The first serious project for a miniature public railway to be organized along the lines of a main-line railway was the Ravenglass and Eskdale Railway in the Lake District of Cumberland. Its time-table had a place in *Bradshaw* also. This little railway was built over the course of an earlier, and at the time derelict, 33-inch gauge line constructed in 1875 for the carriage of hema-tite iron ore and later for passengers. In 1909 it closed down and in 1915 it was leased to a private company. The company converted the seven miles of line to 15-inch gauge, and by the summer of 1915 passengers were being conveyed as far as Murthwaite and later the whole distance to Dalegarth—five miles from Sca Fell. The line is in operation to-day.

Locomotives have been built to suit such gauges as 18-inch, 19-inch (U.S.A.), and 21-inch.

DESIGN NO. 19. 15-INCH GAUGE 'ATLANTIC' LOCOMOTIVE

Scale: 3¼ *inches to the foot.* 4–4–2 *Type*

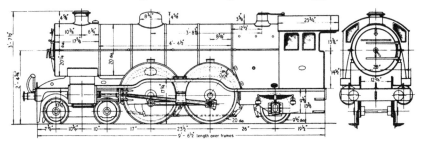

Fig. 35. Greenly's 15-inch Gauge 'Atlantic' Locomotive

The first engine of this type, 'Sans Pareil'—an enlargement of the earlier design—was built by Bassett-Lowke Ltd. for the Geneva Miniature Railway in 1912. The type is still very popular and is recommended for passenger-hauling on a small estate railway. It should be capable of hauling from rest a load of 10 tons.

Specification

Cylinders. (Two outside) 4⅛-inch bore by 6¾-inch stroke. Slide valves on top.
Valve Gear. Stephenson's with rocker arm system to the outside cylinders.
Wheels. Driving and coupled wheels 20-inch diameter. Bogie wheels 9⅜-inch diameter and trailing wheels 10¼-inch diameter. Tender wheels 10¼-inch diameter.
Bogie. Equalized and sprung with side control springs.
Boiler Pressure. 150 lb. per square inch.
Tractive Effort (at 80% boiler pressure). 680 lb.
Length over Locomotive Frames. 9 feet.
Approximate weight of locomotive and tender is 2½ tons.

DESIGN NO. 20. 15-INCH GAUGE 'PACIFIC' LOCOMOTIVE

Scale: $3\frac{1}{4}$ inches to the foot

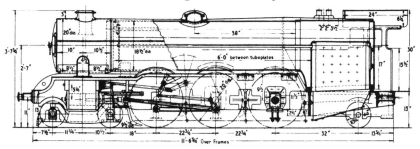

Fig. 36. Greenly's 15-inch Gauge 'Pacific' Locomotive

Following the successful introduction of the 15-inch gauge 'Atlantic' engine 'Sans Pareil', Greenly designed his first 'Pacific' type for the Ravenglass and Eskdale Railway. This engine, named 'Colossus', had two outside cylinders $4\frac{1}{4}$-inch bore by $6\frac{3}{4}$-inch stroke with slide valves on top. As in the case of the 'Atlantic' engine, Stephenson's gear was fitted inside the frames; the valve rods being actuated through rocker arms and levers. The present design (Fig. 35) is a modernized version of one of the earlier 'Pacifics' with Walschaerts' valve gear and piston-valve cylinders.

Specification

Cylinders. (Two) $4\frac{1}{4}$-inch bore by $6\frac{3}{4}$-inch stroke. Piston valves 2-inch diameter. Inside admission.

Main Loco Frames. $\frac{3}{8}$ inch thick by $13\frac{1}{2}$ inches wide.

Boiler. Steel plate throughout to the required B.S. specifications. Barrel $18\frac{1}{2}$-inch diameter. Working pressure 150 lb. per square inch. Hydraulic test pressure (minimum) 225 lb. per square inch.

Tractive Effort at 85% boiler pressure. 765 lb. The estimated hauling capacity on starting is $12\frac{1}{2}$ tons.

Wheels. Coupled 20-inch diameter. Bogie $9\frac{1}{2}$-inch diameter. Trailing $10\frac{1}{4}$-inch. Tender $10\frac{1}{4}$-inch. (Bogie-tender wheels $9\frac{1}{2}$-inch diameter.)

Minimum radius of curve for slow running. 50 yards.

Weight of Locomotive. $2\frac{1}{2}$ tons.

Note. Trailing locomotive axle is mounted on radial axle-boxes to allow displacement on a curved track.

Some of the designs featured in this book were complete and detailed down to the last item, others were more vague and relied on the builder being able to make components off a general layout or from one of the standard parts drawings.

The Greenly archive of drawings, including additional drawings by his daughter Eleonora and her husband Ernest Steel, is being made available by:

Maxitrak/Maidstone Engineering
10/11 Larkstore Park,
Lodge Road,
Staplehurst, Kent.
TN12 0QY.
Great Britain

Telephone: 0044 (0) 1580 893030

Fax : 0044 (0) 1580 891505

Website: www.maxitrak.co.uk

Email: info@maxitrak.co.uk

Contact them direct, or see their website for drawing availability.

INDEX